Semiconductor Logic and Switching Circuits

Samuel L. Oppenheimer

Ohio Technical College

CHARLES E. MERRILL BOOKS, INC., COLUMBUS, OHIO

Library of Congress Catalog Card Number: 66-24955

PRINTED IN THE UNITED STATES OF AMERICA

PREFACE

Semiconductor Logic and Switching Circuits is an attempt to fill the gap that now exists between the many excellent texts on linear semiconductor circuits and those on computers. There are many worthwhile texts in computer basics. These cover computer organization and the arrangement of switching circuits to perform specific computer operations. However, none of these texts tackles the problem that faces the engineering technician. How do these boxes labeled "AND," "Flip-flop," etc., work, and how does one select the components and operating conditions so as to design the circuit?

In addition, switching circuits and logic gates have many applications outside of computers. Many engineering technicians are required to do breadboard designs of switching systems. This text will aid in the design of such systems.

The material contained in this text is adequate for a course in solid state switching circuits. The text assumes that the student has had courses in electronic fundamentals, semiconductor theory, and linear transistor circuits. It should prove useful for students of engineering and technology, and for industrial training programs.

Included in this book are numerous detailed examples. Throughout the text I have tried to steer a middle course between computer and industrial applications of switching circuits. The reader is also encouraged to make full use of his own creative abilities. In the chapter on Applications of Switching Circuits, several problems are stated. Possible solutions to these problems are given, but the reader is encouraged to devise additional different solutions.

Chapter 1 covers the mathematics of logic by using the basic relations and theorems of Boolean algebra. Karnough maps and other simplification routines are avoided. The reader is encouraged to use a straightforward analytical approach to the reduction of switching circuit equations.

iii

Chapters 2, 3, and 4 present a detailed coverage of diode and transistor switching circuit design. Chapter 5 is devoted to the switching circuit applications of tunnel diodes and unijunction transistors. In Chapters 2 and 4 a great deal of attention is given to non-saturated switching—a topic that is often neglected, but one that is of extreme importance in transistor switching circuits.

Chapter 6 covers some applications of the circuits discussed in earlier chapters. Included are some non-computer applications and problems devised to illustrate the wide range of uses for these circuits.

The author is indebted to his colleagues and his students at Ohio Tech and to the many friends in the electronics industries of central Ohio for their constructive suggestions. In particular the suggestions of Mr. Eugene Christopher, of the Electronics Faculty at Ohio Technical College, were most invaluable.

SAMUEL L. OPPENHEIMER

Columbus, Ohio

TABLE OF CONTENTS

Chapter 4

TRANSISTORIZED REGENERATIVE SWITCHING CIRCUITS   64

Chapter 5

SPECIAL SEMICONDUCTOR SWITCHES   117

Chapter 6

APPLICATIONS   151

INDEX   183

CHAPTER 1

The Mathematics
of Switching Circuits

1-1   Introduction

The first application of mathematical logic to switching circuits occurred in 1938. At that time a researcher at Bell Telephone Labs used a form of math known as *Boolean Algebra* in connection with the planning of switching systems and telephone exchanges.

In some respects Boolean algebra is similar to ordinary algebra and arithmetic: Commutative and distributive laws apply, and factoring and expansion are permitted. However, this "algebra" is a mathematics based on variables that have only two possible states. There are no exponents, nor are there any fractions. A variable is either "true" or "false," black or white, yes or no, 0 or 1, etc. One can readily see why this mathematics can offer an attractive method of discussing switching circuits, particularly as applied to digital computers. A switch is either open or closed; there is no permitted "maybe" state for the switch. In digital computers, the logic elements and memory elements have only two possible states—thus, our interest in Boolean algebra.

1-2   OR Logic

In OR logic circuits, we are discussing switching circuits that operate if any one input or any combination of inputs is present. In Figure 1-1 let the closing of a switch be considered an input. It is apparent that an output will occur whenever one or more switches is closed.

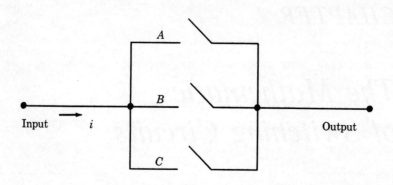

Figure 1-1.   Toggle switch representation of a three-input OR gate.

If we refer to a closed switch as "1" and an open switch as "0," then we must agree that there is current in the output anytime that switches A or B or C equals 1. In Boolean algebra this is written

$$A + B + C = R$$

where the $+$ sign means OR, and R is the result.

1-3   AND Logic

An AND circuit is arranged so that *all* inputs must be present in order to produce an output. Figure 1-2 shows the switches A, B, and C connected in series. All switches must be closed in order to obtain current in the output. The output is obtained when A AND B AND C *all* equal 1. AND is indicated by the various signs of multiplication.

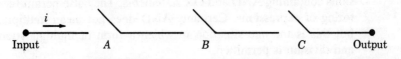

Figure 1-2.   Toggle switch representation of a three-input
                AND gate.

The equation for Figure 1-2 can be written in three ways:

(1) $A \times B \times C = R$
(2) $A \cdot B \cdot C = R$
(3) $ABC = R$

In this book the form shown in (3) will be used.

1-4 Fundamental Rules and Laws

The following list of rules may seem strange to the reader. Understanding them will be easier for us if we first note some guidelines.

GUIDELINES

1. If the same letter is used for more than one variable, we are
   discussing inputs or switches that operate simultaneously.
2. A "1" in an equation means a permanently closed switch, or
   an input that is constantly present.
3. A "0" in an equation means a permanently open switch, or
   an input that is never present.

Rules and Laws:

(a) $A + A = A$ (d) $A \cdot 1 = A$
(b) $AA = A$ (e) $A + 0 = A$
(c) $A \cdot 0 = 0$ (f) $A + 1 = 1$

(g) *Commutative laws:* These laws simply state that the value of an
     expression is not altered by the sequence of the variables.

$$A + B = B + A$$
$$AB = BA$$

(h) *Associative laws:*

$$(A + B) + C = A + (B + C)$$
$$(AB)C = A(BC)$$

(i) *Distributive laws:* These laws permit the expansion of expressions containing AND and OR statements. They also permit factoring of expressions. Certainly AND does not mean multiply, but this is the one situation in which a form of multiplication and division is permitted.

$$(1) \quad A(B + C) = AB + AC$$

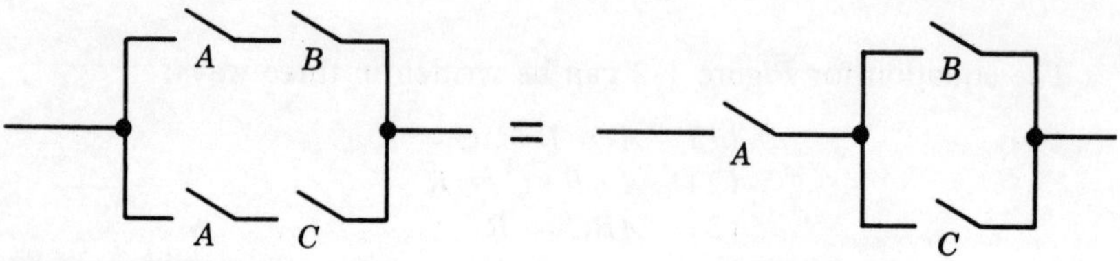

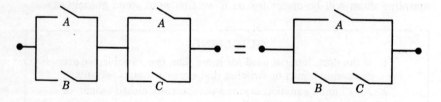

Figure 1-3.

$$(2) \quad (A + B)(A + C) = A + BC$$

Figure. 1-4.

Proof:

$$
\begin{aligned}
(A + B)(A + C) &= AA + AB + AC + BC &&\text{(by expansion)} \\
&= A + AB + AC + BC &&(AA = A) \\
&= A(1 + B + C) + BC &&\text{(by factoring } A) \\
&= A + BC &&(1 + \text{any quantity} = 1, \text{ and} \\
& &&A \cdot 1 = A)
\end{aligned}
$$

1-5 Inversion

Up to this point in our discussion, we have used the concept of switches. In actual practice we will use some form of electronic switching circuit in place of toggle switches. In this case the variables will be inputs to the circuits. These inputs are pulses, either positive or negative. We may then define "1" as some positive pulse (or a negative pulse) and "0" as **the absence of the pulse.** Another possible way of describing 0's and 1's is by *inversion*. If the condition of a variable is stated, then the inverse of the variable is described as the opposite value of the variable. The inverted variable is indicated either by a bar over the letter or by a prime sign. Thus the inverse of D is $\overline{D}$ or D'. In speaking of the inverted variable, we say "not D."

$$1 = 0' \quad \text{and} \quad 0 = 1'$$
$$(\text{If } A = 1, \text{ then } A' = 0; \text{ and if } A' = 1, \text{ then } A = 0.)$$

Rules:

(a) $A + A' = 1$

This is so because it is not possible for both A and A' to be the same value at the same instant. One of the quantities will always equal 1. By rule (f) of Section 1-4, if any input to an OR expression equals 1, the result will equal 1.

(b) $AA' = 0$

This is so because one of the variables must be 0, as both cannot be 1 at the same time. By rule (c) of Section 1-4, if any input to an AND circuit is 0, the result is 0.

(c) $(A')' = A$

In this case, double inversion has occurred and we are back to the uninverted variable.

A classic example of inversion may be seen in the half-adder circuit of a digital computer. When 1 is added to 1 in binary form, the result is 0 in the "one's" column, and a carry of 1 into the next column.

$$0001 + 0001 = 0010$$

Let A be one of the inputs to a half-adder, and B the other input. When both A and B are 0, the sum is 0. If A is 1 and B is 0, or if B is 1 and A is 0, then the sum is 1 and the carry is 0. However, if both A and B are 1, then the sum ("one's" column) is 0 and the carry is 1.

$$0000 + 0000 = 0000$$
$$0001 + 0000 = 0001$$
$$0000 + 0001 = 0001$$
$$0001 + 0001 = 0010$$

In Boolean algebra, the equations of the half-adder are:

$$\text{Sum} = AB' + A'B$$
$$\text{Carry} = AB$$

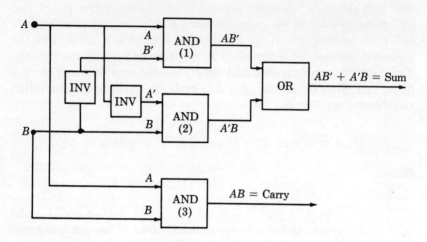

Figure 1-5.   Half-adder.

Figure 1-5 is a block diagram of a circuit that will perform the functions of a half-adder.

Note that the inputs of the half-adder do not include either of the inverted quantities. Pulse sources usually do not provide both inverted and normal inputs. To obtain A' and B', inverters are used. When an input is 1, the output of the inverter is 0. If the input is 0 (the absence of a pulse), the output of the inverter is 1. Let us now go through the operation of the half-adder using pulses.

1. $A = 0, B = 0$. None of the AND gates operates because at least one input to each circuit is zero. *Carry* is 0 because it is derived directly from the output of an AND gate. The *sum* is zero because both of the inputs to the OR gate are zero.

2. $A = 1, B = 0$. AND gate 1 operates and supplies a 1 input to the OR gate. A is a 1 input to the AND gate, and B' is 1 because $B = 0$. AND gate 2 does not operate because both inputs to this gate are zero. AND gate 3 does not operate because one of its inputs is zero. There is no *carry*, but the *sum* is 1 since either input to an OR gate will produce an output of 1.

3. $A = 0, B = 1$. The explanation is the same as for step 2. AND gates 1 and 3 are inoperative, and AND gate 2 supplies a 1 input to the OR gate. Hence, the *sum* is 1 and the *carry* is zero.

4. $A = 1, B = 1$. AND gates 1 and 2 cannot operate because the in-

verters supply 0's to both gates. The *sum* is zero. There is a carry of 1 because both inputs to AND gate 3 are 1's.

1-6 NOR and NAND Gates

These are logic circuit gates whose rules of operation are similar to OR and AND gates. However, the NOR and NAND circuits supply inverted outputs. In the OR circuit if any input is 1, the output is 1. In the NOR circuit if any input is 1, the output is 0. The only time that the output of a NOR gate is 1 is when all of the inputs to the gate are 0. The reader might note the similarity between the requirements for a 1 output of a NOR circuit and the requirements for a 1 output of an AND circuit. In both cases all inputs must be the same. In the NAND circuit, a 1 output is obtained so long as any input to the gate is 0. A 0 output is supplied whenever all inputs to the NAND gate are 1. In this respect the NAND gate behaves similarly to the OR gate, in that not all inputs must be present to get a 1 output. The NOR and NAND gates may be viewed as OR and AND circuits *followed by inverters*. In actual practice it is a simple matter to make the gate perform both the logic function and inversion without the need for a separate inverter. An important theorem of circuit simplification is based upon these concepts.

1-7 De Morgan's Theorem

If all of the variables of an equation are inverted, and all of the logical connectives are switched and inverted (NAND for OR and NOR for AND), the resulting equation is equal to the original equation.

$$
\begin{array}{ll}
\text{(i)} & A + B = (A'B')' \\
\text{(ii)} & AB = (A' + B')' \\
\text{(iii)} & A + B' = (A'B)' \\
\text{(iv)} & A'B = (A + B')'
\end{array}
$$

The reader will note that De Morgan's theorem is simply a restatement of Section 1-6. Statements (i) and (ii) are the classical form of the theorem. The most direct proof of the theorem is by use of "truth table." The truth table is a tabular display of the various combinations obtained when each variable is in one of its possible states. *In any truth table the number of possible combinations of the variables is 2^n, where n is the number of variables.* In the proof of statements (i) and (ii) there are four combinations possible since there are only the two variables A and B.

Proof that $A + B = (A'B')'$

A	B	$A+B$	A'	B'	$A'B'$	$(A'B')'$
0	0	0	1	1	1	0
1	0	1	0	1	0	1
0	1	1	1	0	0	1
1	1	1	0	0	0	1

$A + B$ correlates perfectly with $(A'B')'$ for each combination of variables.

Proof that $AB = (A' + B')'$

A	B	AB	A'	B'	$A'+B'$	$(A'+B')'$
0	0	0	1	1	1	0
1	0	0	0	1	1	0
0	1	0	1	0	1	0
1	1	1	0	0	0	1

AB correlates perfectly with $(A' + B')'$ for each combination of variables.

De Morgan's theorem is particularly attractive for use with transistor logic circuits. AND gates using transistors are cumbersome and require the use of one transistor for each variable. NOR logic and inverters will perform the same functions with a considerable savings in the number of transistors needed. This will be developed fully in succeeding chapters.

Example 1.1. Given the following equation, apply De Morgan's theorem to obtain an equivalent equation. Illustrate both circuits with a block diagram.

$$AB(D + E') = R, \quad \text{or expanding,} \quad ABD + ABE' = R$$

Solution:

$$[(A' + B' + D')'(A' + B' + E)']' = R$$

Figure 1-6 illustrates the logic circuits for both equations in block form.

Example 1.2. Prove by the use of De Morgan's theorem that $A + A'B = A + B$.

Solution:

(a) Apply the theorem to the left side of the equation:

$$[A'(A + B')']'$$

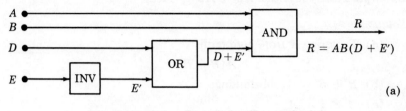

Figure 1-6(a).   Circuit for Example 1.1.

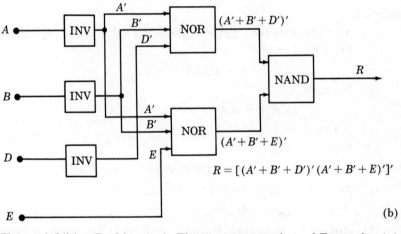

Figure 1-6(b).   De Morgan's Theorem expansion of Example 1.1.

(b) Expand by "multiplying" the binomial by A'.

$$(A'A + A'B')'$$

(c) $A'A = 0$ and is dropped, which leaves:

(d) $(A'B')'$

(e) The quantity in (d) is the NAND equivalent of $A + B$.

1-8   Simplification of Equations

The following examples will illustrate the applications of the rules and theorems to the reduction of Boolean equations.

Example 1.3. Prove that $AB + AB' = A$.

Solution:

(a) Factoring A from both terms:

$$A(B + B')$$

(b) $B + B' = 1$; substituting:

(c) $A \times 1 = A$

Example 1.4. Without using De Morgan's theorem, demonstrate that $A + B = A + A'B$.

Solution:

(a) Multiplication by 1 cannot change the value of an expression. Let 1 be $A + A'$.

$$(A + B)(A + A')$$

(b) Expanding:

$$AA + AA' + AB + A'B$$

(c) $AA = A$ and $AA' = 0$.

(d) Rewriting (b):

$$A + AB + A'B$$

(e) Factoring A from the first two terms:

$$A(1 + B) + A'B$$

(f) $A(1 + B)$ reduces to A since $1 + B = 1$. The resulting equation is then:

$$A + A'B$$

Example 1.5. Simplify the following expression:

$$(G + F)(G + A) = R$$

Solution:

(a) Expanding the expression:

$$GG + GA + FG + FA = R$$

(b) Factor G from the first three terms:

$$G(1 + A + F) + FA = R$$

(c) The term inside the parentheses equals 1 and is dropped:

$$R = G + FA$$

Example 1.6. Simplify the following expression:
$$(A + B)(A + D)(C + B')$$

Solution:

Expansion of the expression is accomplished in two steps. The first two binomials are combined, then this resulting expression is reduced. The resultant is combined by expansion with the third binomial.

(a) $(A + B)(A + D)$
$AA + AD + AB + BD$
$A + AD + AB + BD$
$A(1 + D + B) + BD$
$A + BD$

(b) $(A + BD)(C + B')$
$AC + AB' + BDC + B'BD$
$A(C + B') + BCD$

Note that $B'BD$ drops out since $B'B = 0$.

Example 1.7. Simplify the following expression:
$$(X + Y)(X + D)(Z + Y)(Z + D) = R$$

Solution:

The method of solution is the same as in the preceding example.

(a) $(X + Y)(X + D)$
$XX + XD + XY + DY$
$X + XD + XY + DY$
$X(1 + D + Y) + DY$
$X + DY$

(b) $(Z + Y)(Z + D)$
$ZZ + ZD + ZY + DY$
$Z + ZD + ZY + DY$
$Z(1 + D + Y) + DY$
$Z + DY$

(c) $(X + DY)(Z + DY)$
$XZ + XDY + ZDY + DYDY$
$XZ + DY(X + Z + 1)$
$XZ + DY = R$

An interesting aspect of the simplification of equations is a *partial* application of De Morgan's theorem. It is not mandatory that the theorem be applied to every part of an expression. De Morgan's theorem can be applied to terms of an equation without being applied to every term. By this method a logic equation can be reduced to terms consisting only of OR and NOR gates. In the design of actual circuits the ability to eliminate AND circuits can be of considerable advantage. The reader probably observed that the example of an application of De Morgan's theorem (Example 1.1) resulted in a more complicated equation than the original equation. However, if De Morgan's theorem is applied to only a part of the expression, a much simpler expression is obtained. We shall repeat the expression of Example 1.1, but will avoid the use of a NAND circuit.

$$AB(D + E') = R$$
$$ABD + ABE' = R$$
$$(A' + B' + D')' + (A' + B' + E')' = R$$

The resulting expression contains neither AND nor NAND circuits, and would be a very simple logic circuit to construct using only inverters, OR circuits, and NOR circuits.

PROBLEMS

1.1. (a) Draw the logic block diagram for the following equation.
$$AB + C(D + E) = R$$

(b) What is the total number of possible combinations of the variables that would be needed to complete a truth table?

1.2. Reduce the following expression.
$$XY(X + D) + YD = R$$

1.3. What is the equation for the circuit of Figure 1-7?

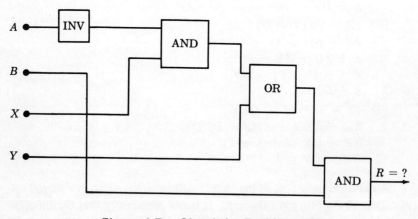

Figure 1-7.   Circuit for Problem 1.3.

1.4. Apply De Morgan's theorem to the following expression so that only inverters, OR, and NOR gates are used.

$$\mu\beta(\alpha + \pi) + \sigma\epsilon = \Delta$$

1.5. The binary counter in Figure 1-8 consists of 2 stages. The output terminals for each step of the count are shown. Write the equations for the decimal readout system for counts 1, 2, and 3, given that decimal $0 = AB'C'D'$.

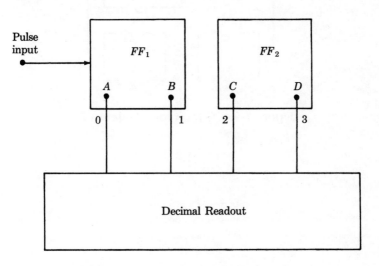

Figure 1-8.   Circuit for Problem 1.5.

1.6. A missile checkout system includes the checking of the following variables: (a) If X is present, Y and Z must not be present. (b) If Y is present, Z must be present and X cannot be present. Write the logic equation for the checkout system.

1.7. Reduce the following equation.

$$A(CD + BE) + A'CD + BA'E$$

1.8. Write the equation for the switching circuit of Figure 1-9.

1.9. Let X be the ignition switch in an automobile. Let Y be the motor, and Z the generator warning light on the dashboard. Assuming that there are no mechanical failures, write the logic equations for the possible combinations of X, X', Y, Y', Z and Z' that will produce acceptable results.

1.10. Write the equations for the binary half-adder so that only NOR and OR circuits will be used.

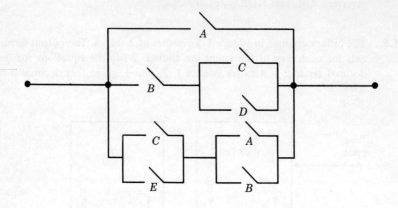

Figure 1-9.   Circuit for Problem 1.8.

CHAPTER 2

Semiconductor Switches

2-1 Switches

The basic requirement of a good switch is that there be a distinct and constant difference between the open and closed states of the switch. Switches can be toggles, relays, commutators, etc. Obviously, mechanical switches approach the theoretical ideal of infinite resistance when open and zero resistance when closed. However, mechanical switches fail to meet our needs when we consider switching as applied to digital computers. To be of practical value in the digital computer, the switching circuit must be capable of performing many thousands of operations per second and also be capable of switching in a time interval measured in fractions of a microsecond, or less. The mechanical switch fails to meet the needs for high speed and long life. Some mechanical switching is still used in older computers, but even there it is used only in the input system like the old punched card readers. Even telephone exchanges are changing from relays to semiconductor circuits.

Semiconductor devices can be used as switches. These offer the attractive combination of great reliability and the capability of very high speed operation. Semiconductors can be operated in such a manner that only two states of operation are available to the device. One is a state of high current flow with low voltage drop, the other a state of low current flow with high voltage drop.

2-2 The Junction Transistor Switch

Figure 2-1 is an elementary circuit of a transistor switching circuit. The transistor is in cutoff until a positive voltage pulse is applied to the input terminal. When cut off, the only collector current flow is due to $(1 + h_{FE})I_{CO}$, and the collector-to-emitter voltage, V_{CE}, is approximately equal to V_{CC}. When the pulse is applied to the base, the collector current increases. The amount of increase in I_C is a function of base current.

$$I_C = h_{FE}I_B + (1 + h_{FE}I_{CO}) \qquad (2\text{-}1)$$

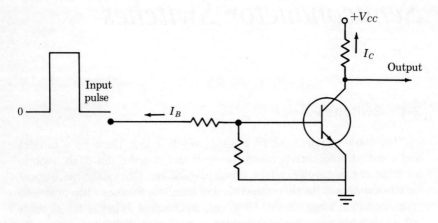

Figure 2-1. Common emitter switch.

Figure 2-2 shows a set of typical collector characteristics in the CE configuration. Region I is called the *cut-off region* and is defined as that region where both junctions are reverse biased. Region II is the *active region*. This is the region of normal operation for any transistor amplifier. The collector junction is reverse biased, and the emitter junction is forward biased. Region III is called the *saturation region*. In this region both junctions are forward biased.

If a load line for the circuit of Figure 2-1 is drawn on the characteristics of Figure 2-2, it is apparent that the transistor can be made to switch between sets of definite operating points. With the circuit shown, it is possible to switch from the border of region I to any point in region II or to points in region III. By the addition of some amount of fixed forward bias it is possible to switch the circuit from OFF to ON while confining all operation to region II. If some amount of reverse bias is used, the transistor circuit can be made to switch from region I to either region II or region III.

Highest switching speeds are obtained when the operation of the circuit is confined to region II. Here the unit is never completely cut off, nor is it permitted to draw enough current to switch into region III. The price paid for this high speed switching is greater complexity and smaller output voltage for a given value of V_{CC}. Maximum output of the circuit is obtained when the transistor is switched from region I to region III.

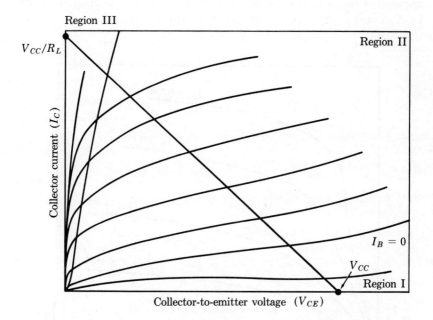

Figure 2-2. Static collector characteristics of a junction transistor.

Operation of a transistor switch from border to border of region II is known as *fulldriven* operation. *Overdriven* operation causes saturation when ON, and is from region I to region III.

2-3 The Saturated Switch

The collector characteristics of Figure 2-2 do not accurately display the saturation region. Figure 2-3 expands the set of CE collector characteristics in the saturation region. The reader will note that values of V_{CE} vary from a few millivolts to about 250 mv. In a junction transistor with such low values of V_{CE}, the collector becomes forward biased with respect to the base. Both the emitter and the collector inject minority charge carriers into the base. Because the rate of recombination in the base is much less than the rate with which charges are being emitted into the base, charges are stored in the base. When a junction transistor is operated as a saturated switch, the storage of charge in the base has a pronounced effect upon the transient response of the unit. Collector current flow cannot drop until the stored excess charges are swept out of the base. The time required for the removal of the stored excess charge is called *storage time delay*. This will be discussed in detail in the section on transient response.

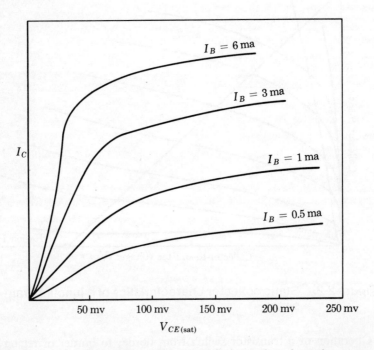

Figure 2-3. Saturation characteristics of a junction transistor.

The resistance of the unit from collector to emitter is very low when in saturation. Values vary from as low as 1 Ω in germanium alloy transistors, 1.2 Ω in silicon planar expitaxial transistors, to less than 5 Ω in germanium mesa transistors. The value of saturation resistance for a particular value of collector current is defined by the following equation:

$$r_{CE(\text{sat})} = \frac{V_{CE(\text{sat})}}{I_C} \tag{2-2}$$

Operation at saturation has various advantages and disadvantages. In addition to storage time delay, saturated operation of the transistor makes the switch sensitive to very small signal levels. Because there is very little difference between $V_{BE(\text{sat})}$ and $V_{CE(\text{sat})}$, small signals can cause the switch to be erratic. However, storage time delay makes the saturated switching circuit relatively immune to transients of short duration. Another problem with operation at saturation is the possibility of destructive currents if the emitter becomes reverse biased at high temperatures. When an OFF pulse is applied to the switch, the emitter becomes reverse biased. Due to storage time delay, the collector is still forward biased. The collector now behaves as an emitter, and the emitter as a collector. Germanium units should not be operated as saturated switches at temperatures greater than 40°C. The temperature limit for silicon transistors used as saturated switches should never exceed 150°C. Against the problems so far discussed, we do have the major advantages of simplicity of design and large and definite levels of output voltages. Where high speed switching is not required, saturated switching is widely used.

The design of the saturated switch is straightforward. A value of base drive current is selected so that there will be sufficient collector current flow to insure that saturation occurs. It is important to note that after an initial increase, h_{FE} decreases with increasing collector currents. Figure 2-4 illustrates the variation of h_{FE} with I_C. Curves of this type are usually available for the various transistors that have been especially designed for switching applications.

The first step in the design of the switch is to determine I_C. In making the computation for I_C, it is assumed that $V_{CE(\text{sat})}$ is so small that no appreciable error is introduced if it is allowed to be zero. With this assumption, all of V_{CC} must be dropped across the load resistance when the transistor is in saturation:

$$I_{C(\text{sat})} = \frac{V_{CC}}{R_L} \tag{2-3}$$

Once $I_{C(\text{sat})}$ is known, h_{FE} is determined from the curves of h_{FE}/I_C. Then $I_{B(\text{min})}$ can be found:

$$I_{B(\text{min})} = \frac{I_{C(\text{sat})}}{h_{FE}} \tag{2-4}$$

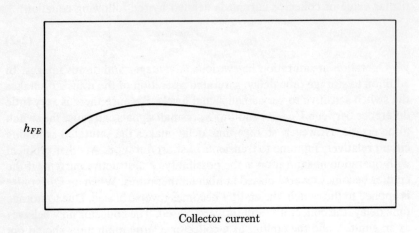

Figure 2-4. Variation of h_{FE} with collector current in a junction transistor.

Good design practice calls for the value of base drive current used in the circuit to be larger than that of the base current determined by Eq. (2-4). This overdrive current insures that saturation will occur regardless of variations between transistors of the same type, and also improves the transient response of the switch.

Example 2.1. The circuit of Figure 2-5 is to be switched between cutoff and saturation. Calculate the necessary value of R_B if the input pulse varies from 0 to -2 v.

Solution:

(a) Calculate $I_{C(\text{sat})}$.

$$I_{C(\text{sat})} = \frac{V_{CC}}{R_L} = \frac{-30}{1800} = -16.7 \text{ ma}$$

(b) Determine h_{FE}. In this example let $h_{FE} = 36$.

(c) Calculate $I_{B(\text{min})}$.

$$I_{B(\text{min})} = \frac{I_{C(\text{sat})}}{h_{FE}} = \frac{-16.7 \times 10^{-3}}{36} = -0.463 \text{ ma}$$

(d) R_B is found in the following manner.

$$I_B = 3[I_{B(\text{min})}] = -1.39 \text{ ma}$$

$$R_B = \frac{E_{\max}}{I_B} = \frac{-2}{-1.39 \times 10^{-3}} = 1440 \text{ } \Omega$$

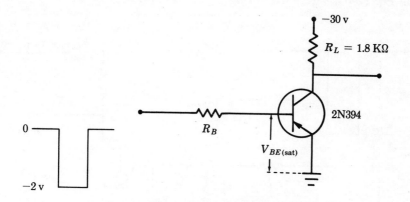

Figure 2-5. Circuit for Example 2.1.

The reader will note that all of the input pulse was assumed to be dropped across R_B. This approach is both common and valid. In many cases, $V_{BE(sat)}$ will not be listed in the transistor specifications. Also, $V_{BE(sat)}$ is much smaller than the amplitude of the pulse, E_{max}. In the event that the pulse amplitude is so small that the drop between base and emitter at saturation is a factor that must be considered, Eq. (2-5) will suffice.

$$R_B = \frac{E_{max} - |V_{BE(sat)}|}{I_B} \tag{2-5}$$

The reader is also reminded that the value of I_B used in the design is three times as large as the amount needed for saturation, so that even though $V_{BE(sat)}$ subtracts from the pulse input, there is sufficient drive to insure saturation.

Accurate design of the circuit of Figure 2-6 requires that $V_{BE(sat)}$ be known. The solution for R_B is made in the following order:

$$I_2 = \frac{V_{BB} + V_{BE(sat)}}{R_1}$$
$$I_1 = I_B + I_2$$
$$R_B = \frac{E_{max} - |V_{BE(sat)}|}{I_1} \tag{2-6}$$

The overdriven switch of Figure 2-6 may be designed with success even if $V_{BE(sat)}$ is not specified. The typical drop across the base-to-emitter junction of a germanium transistor is about 300 mv, and for a silicon transistor the drop is about 700 mv. These values may be safely assumed in Eq. (2-6).

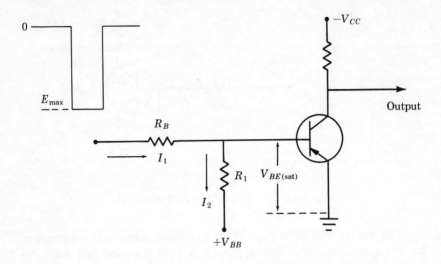

Figure 2-6. Overdriven switch.

2-4 Transient Response

When the transistor is switched between OFF and ON states by a rectangular pulse, the response of the switch to the pulse is not rectangular. The concepts involved in understanding why the switch does not faithfully follow the waveshape of the pulse is the problem devoted to transient response.

Consider that a transistor is biased in region I. The unit is in cutoff, and the base-to-emitter junction and the collector-to-base junction are reverse biased. The charge on the base-to-emitter junction capacitance, C_{eb}, is equal to the bias. The charge on the collector-to-base junction capacitance, C_{cb}, is the sum of the base bias voltage and the collector supply voltage. In Figure 2-6 assume that V_{BB} is 5 volts and V_{CC} is -25 volts. The charge on C_{eb} equals 5 volts and the charge on C_{cb} equals 30 volts. When a negative pulse is applied to the input terminal, it is not possible for the base to become forward biased until C_{eb} is discharged. It is also necessary for the collector capacitance to discharge before there can be a drop across the load resistance. In addition to the time needed to discharge the junction capacitances, time is required in order for diffusion of charges from the emitter to the collector to begin.

If the switch is an overdriven switch, then excess minority carriers are stored in the base and, to some extent, in the collector while the switch is in saturation. At the time the pulse goes positive to shut off the switch, current continues to flow in the collector and base circuits. Current flow continues in the collector circuit until all minority carriers are removed from the base. Current flow does not even begin to decrease in the collector circuit until the base is cleared of minority carriers. The collector current then decreases gradually as the charge on the base reverses and shuts off the transistor.

The result of the ideas stated in the preceding two paragraphs is that the collector voltage and current waveforms cannot be rectangular, but take the general shape shown in Figure 2-7. Figure 2-7 details the voltage and current waveshapes for the base and collector of an overdriven switch.

The reader will note that the curve for collector current shows some time intervals with specific designations.

t_d The time required for i_c to rise to 10% of its maximum value. This is called *delay time*, and is due to the junction capacitances, external resistances including the load resistance, and the time required for drift and/or diffusion of charge from emitter to collector.

t_r This is called *rise time*, and is the time required for collector current to reach 90% of maximum value.

t_s The time required from the application of an OFF pulse (or the removal of the ON pulse) for collector current to drop from 100% to 90%. This time is due to charge storage when in saturation and is called *storage time delay*.

t_f *Fall time.* The time needed for collector current to drop from 90% to 10% of maximum.

Common practice calls for the above time designations to be used with collector voltage rather than current. The same definitions apply, but the percentages are applied in terms of maximum voltage rather than current.

By a careful selection of components, and the proper choice of base drive, it is possible to reduce both storage time delay and the delay time when turning on the transistor.

In order to reduce rise time, it is necessary to keep external base circuit resistance low and to use more voltage than needed to turn on the transistor. Obviously, the time constant of the charging circuit is kept low when external resistances are as small as possible. Figure 2-8 shows why overdriving the base ON reduces t_d. The time constant is the same, with

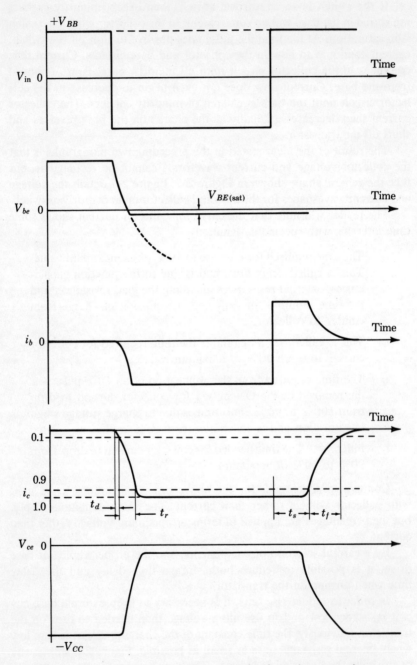

Figure 2-7. Transient response of a junction transistor.

or without overdriving the base. When the input pulse is just enough to turn on the unit, then it becomes apparent that much of the exponential rise of voltage is needed to reach a suitable value of V_{BE}. With excess pulse voltage, the proper value of V_{BE} is reached during the fast rising, linear portion of the charging curve.

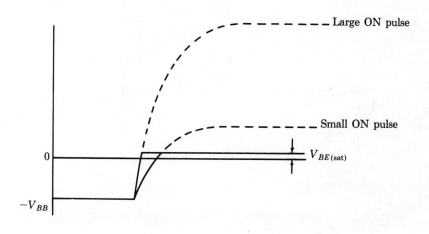

Figure 2-8. A large drive pulse reduces delay time.

Storage time delay can be reduced by using a large amount of reverse bias on the base. This helps to remove charges from the base, permitting a more rapid shutoff. However, the use of reverse bias causes C_{eb} to have a greater charge on it when turn ON is attempted, which will increase t_d. Usually, storage time is the greater problem, so that reversing the base voltage is a good technique.

Turn-on time can be further reduced by the use of a capacitor across the base bias resistor. A capacitor cannot change charge instantaneously, and when a pulse is applied to the input, the capacitor appears as a short across the resistor. Full pulse voltage is immediately applied to the base, nearly completely eliminating t_d. Best results are obtained when the time constant of the drive circuit is equal to the time constant of the base-emitter junction. The time constant of the base-emitter junction is not readily available, but is equal to the effective lifetime of charges in the base when the base is forward biased. For a typical alloy junction transistor this is in the order of 10^{-6} seconds. This method of speeding up performance is shown in Figure 2-9 for a NPN transistor.

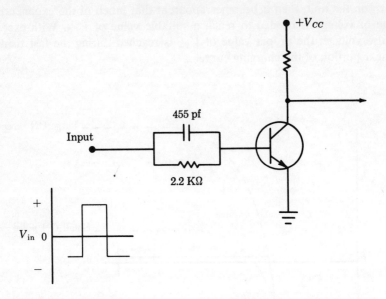

Figure 2-9.   Capacitance across the base resistor reduces
delay time.

It should be apparent by now that the greatest problem in high speed switching is that of storage time delay. Highest switching speeds are obtained when the unit is overdriven ON so that the turn ON is fast, but is prevented from saturating, so that storage time delay is completely removed.

2-5 Non-Saturated Switching

Various clamping techniques can be used to prevent saturation. Some are complex and result in excellent results; others are relatively simple and do not provide much improvement in response over the saturated switch.

Collector voltage clamping prevents V_{CE} from becoming less than V_{BE}. The diode of Figure 2-10 is connected to a source equal to the desired clamp level. When the transistor is OFF, the diode is back biased. When the switch is pulsed ON, V_{CE} drops. At the voltage level where V_{CE} is slightly less than V_{CL}, the diode conducts and clamps the collector

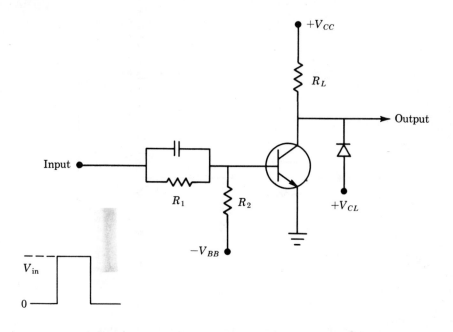

Figure 2-10. Collector voltage clamping.

voltage. This method of clamping does not result in much improvement in response time. The collector current is still a function of I_B, and reaches a higher level than in the saturated switch. The diode is simply acting as the load for the transistor. In addition, the diode may have a long recovery time because of the high currents through it. Figure 2-11 shows the current paths during the clamp period. The load line of Figure 2-12 shows how the diode changes the effective load, but does not limit collector current.

In the circuit of Figure 2-11 the collector current is the sum of the currents I_L and I_D. I_L is found by use of Eq. (2-7).

$$I_L = \frac{V_{cc} - V_{cL}}{R_L} \qquad (2\text{-}7)$$

The current I_D is the difference between the collector current and I_L.

$$I_D = h_{FE}I_B - \frac{V_{cc} - V_{cL}}{R_L} \qquad (2\text{-}8)$$

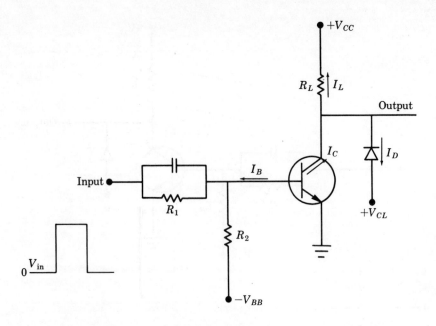

Figure 2-11.　Current paths during the clamp period.

A more effective technique is *collector current clamping*. In the circuit of Figure 2-13, the diode is back biased until the input pulse turns on the switch. When V_{CE} becomes less than V_D, the diode "fires" and increases the current through R_1. When the drop across R_1 increases, the voltage across R_2 must decrease. The base current is proportional to the drop across R_2 and, therefore, decreases. Because the collector current is $h_{FE}I_B$, the collector current is limited to some specific value.

ANALYSIS:

The analysis of the circuit is based upon the following assumptions:

$$(1) \quad R_2 \gg h_{IB}$$
$$(2) \quad R_1 \gg R_L$$
$$(3) \quad V_{CE(clamp)} \gg V_{BE}$$

Figure 2-14 shows the equivalent circuit at the time of clamp. It is assumed that the drop across the diode is negligible.

a.　$I_B = V_{CE}/R_2$　　　　　　　　　　　　　　　　　　　　(2-9)

b.　$I_C = h_{FE}I_B$

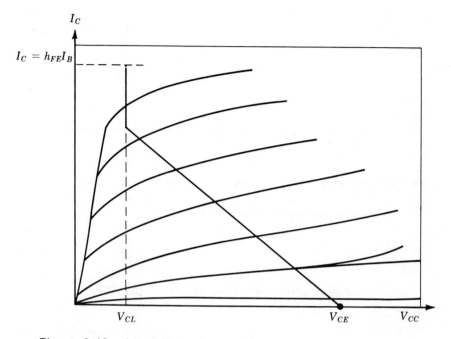

Figure 2-12.   Load line when collector voltage clamping is used.

c. $I_C = \dfrac{h_{FE} V_{CE}}{R_2}$ (2-10)

d. $V_{CE} = V_{CC} - I_C R_L$ (2-11)

$\qquad = V_{CC} - \dfrac{h_{FE} V_{CE} R_L}{R_2}$

$\qquad = \dfrac{R_2 V_{CC}}{R_2 + h_{FE} R_L}$ (2-12)

e.   Equation (2-12) can be rearranged to obtain R_2.

$$R_2 = \frac{V_{CE} h_{FE} R_L}{V_{CC} - V_{CE}} \qquad\qquad \text{(2-13)}$$

f.   Collector current can be found for a particular clamping level by substituting Eq. (2-12) into Eq. (2-10).

$$I_C = \frac{h_{FE} V_{CC}}{R_2 + h_{FE} R_L} \qquad\qquad \text{(2-14)}$$

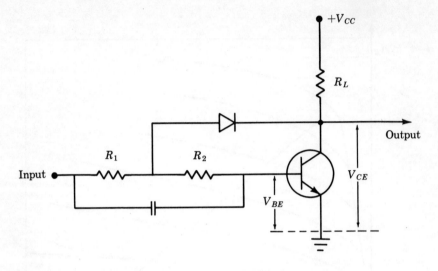

Figure 2-13.   Collector current clamping.

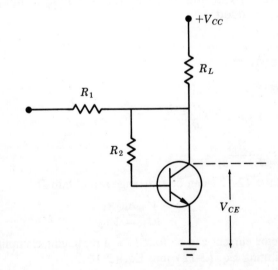

Figure 2-14.   Equivalent circuit of collector current clamping during the clamp interval.

Example 2.2. A type 2N2193 transistor is used in the circuit of Figure 2-13. Assume that $h_{FE(min)} = 15$, $V_{CC} = 30$ v, $V_{CE(clamp)} = 3.5$ v, and $R_L = 680$ ohms. The input pulse swings from -15 v to $+15$ v. Calculate R_2, R_1, I_B, and I_C.

Solution:

(a) R_2 is found by use of Eq. (2-13).

$$R_2 = \frac{3.5 \times 15 \times 680}{30 - 3.5} = 1350 \ \Omega$$

(b) I_C can now be found [(Eq. (2-14)].

$$I_C = \frac{15 \times 30}{1.35 \times 10^3 + 10.2 \times 10^3} = 52 \text{ ma}$$

(c) $I_B = I_C/h_{FE} = 52 \times 10^{-3}/15 = 3.46 \text{ ma}$

(d) The base current is determined by the ratio of the forward portion of the input voltage ($+15$ v) to the total resistance of $R_1 + R_2$. Therefore:

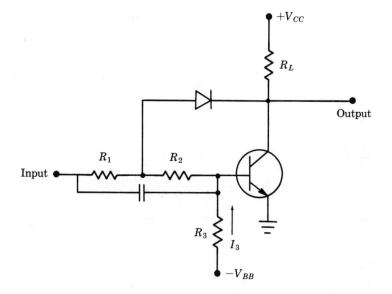

Figure 2-15.   Collector current clamping with a base voltage source.

$$R_1 = \frac{+V_{in}}{I_B} - R_2$$

$$= \frac{15}{3.46 \times 10^3} - 1350 = 3000 \ \Omega$$

A particularly attractive method of I_C clamping, especially for use with bistable multivibrators, is shown in Figure 2-15. The added reverse-bias circuit and resistor R_3 help to make the current clamp point less dependent upon h_{FE}.

ANALYSIS (at time of clamp):

a. The same assumptions are made as for the circuit of Figure 2-13. In addition, it is assumed that $V_{BB} \gg V_{BE}$.

b. $I_3 = \dfrac{V_{BB}}{R_3}$

c. $V_{CE} = R_2(I_3 + I_B)$ \hfill (2-15)

d. $V_{CE} = V_{CC} - I_C R_L$

e. Solve Eq. (2-15) for I_B.

$$I_B = \frac{V_{CE} - R_2 I_3}{R_2} \tag{2-16}$$

f. $I_C = h_{FE}I_B$

$$= \frac{h_{FE}V_{CE} - h_{FE}R_2I_3}{R_2} \tag{2-17}$$

g. $V_{CE} = V_{CC} - \dfrac{h_{FE}R_LV_{CE} - h_{FE}R_LR_2I_3}{R_2}$ \hfill (2-18)

h. Solve Eq. (2-18) for V_{CE}.

$$V_{CE} = \frac{R_2(V_{CC} + h_{FE}R_LI_3)}{R_2 + h_{FE}R_L} \tag{2-19}$$

i. Equation (2-19) may be solved for R_2.

$$R_2 = \frac{h_{FE}R_LV_{CE}}{V_{CC} - V_{CE} + h_{FE}R_LI_3} \tag{2-20}$$

Example 2.3.   Repeat the conditions of Example 2.2 for the circuit of Figure 2-16. Solve for R_1, R_2, I_B, I_C, and C.

Solution:

(a) $I_3 = V_{BB}/R_3 = 6/2 \times 10^3 = 3$ ma.

(b) R_2 is found by use of Eq. (2-20).

$$R_2 = \frac{15 \times 680 \times 3.5}{26.5 + 15 \times 680 \times 3 \times 10^{-3}} = 625 \ \Omega$$

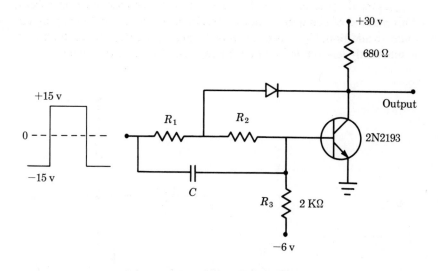

Figure 2-16. Circuit for Example 2.3.

(c) I_B is found by use of Eq. (2-16).

$$I_B = \frac{3.5 - 625 \times 3 \times 10^{-3}}{625} = 2.6 \text{ ma}$$

(d) $I_C = h_{FE}I_B$

$$= 15 \times 2.6 \times 10^{-3} = 39.1 \text{ ma}$$

(e) $R_1 = \frac{+V_{\text{in}}}{I_B + I_3} - R_2$

$$= \frac{15}{5.6 \times 10^{-3}} - 625 = 2000 \ \Omega \text{ (approx)}$$

(f) C is found by making the time constant $C(R_1 + R_2)$ equal 1 μsec.

$$C = \frac{10^{-6}}{0.2625 \times 10^4} = 380 \text{ pf}$$

Double diode clamping is a means of clamping collector current and voltage by making use of the constant voltage properties of silicon and diode germanium diodes. The circuit of Figure 2-17 contains a silicon diode in the base circuit. When forward biased, there is a constant drop of 700 mv across the silicon diode. When collector voltage drops to less than 0.7 volt, the germanium diode conducts and "shorts" the collector to the N side of the silicon diode; V_{CE} is therefore clamped at 0.7 volt. At the same time, current flow through the germanium diode and R_1 increases the drop across R_1, reducing the drive to the base of the transistor. This method of clamping is not as precise as in the current clamping circuits. In addition, V_{CE} is not appreciably larger than V_{BE}; hence, the circuit is inherently less stable and may be switched by small transients.

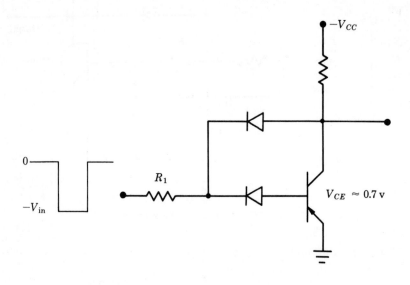

Figure 2-17.   Double diode clamping.

Up to this point, all discussion of non-saturating switches has been based upon turning a switch ON, yet preventing the switch from operating in the saturated region. It is also possible to devise a non-saturated switch that does not use any clamping techniques. In this case, the switch is turned OFF by the application of the input pulse. Figure 2-18 illustrates a typical circuit of this type.

Turn-off time is quite small because the base is forward biased prior to the application of the input pulse. Emitter-to-base capacitance is quite high, but it is shunted by the very low input resistance of the transistor. The time required for the switch to turn ON after the input pulse drops to zero is also quite low. During the OFF interval, full pulse voltage is applied to the base of the transistor. This is so because the back-biased base represents a resistance many times greater than R_1. The capacitance C_{eb} is charged to this voltage. When the input pulse drops to zero, C_{eb}

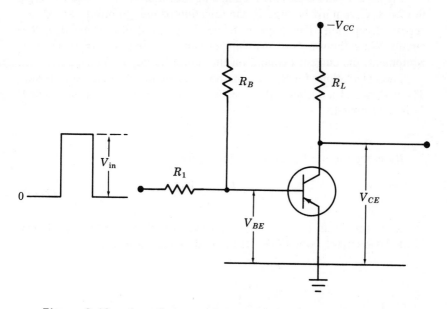

Figure 2-18.   Junction transistor switch with pulse turn off.

discharges through R_B. Because R_B is returned to the collector supply, the discharge is rapid. The time required to discharge C_{eb} to zero can be determined by the following equations.

$$0 = (|V_{CC}| + V_{in})(1 - \epsilon^{-t/R_B C_{eb}}) - V_{in} \qquad \textbf{(2-21)}$$

$$1 - \epsilon^{-t/R_B C_{eb}} = \frac{V_{in}}{|V_{CC}| + V_{in}} \qquad \textbf{(2-22)}$$

Solving for t:

$$t = R_B C_{eb} \ln\left(1 + \frac{V_{in}}{|V_{CC}|}\right) \qquad \textbf{(2-23)}$$

Example 2.4.   The circuit of Figure 2-18 is assumed to have the following operation: $R_B = 22$ KΩ, $C_{eb} = 20$ pf, $V_{in} = 6$ v, and $V_{CC} = -24$ v. Determine the time needed for C_{eb} to discharge to zero volts.

Solution:

$$
\begin{aligned}
t &= (22 \times 10^3 \times 20 \times 10^{-12}) \ln(1 + 6/24) \\
&= 440 \times 10^{-9} \times \ln 1.25 \\
&= 440 \times 10^{-9} \times 0.223 \\
&= 98.3 \text{ nsec}
\end{aligned}
$$

Figure 2-19 illustrates the load line of operation for the circuit of Figure 2-18. Care must be used in the selection of the Q point to avoid excessive dissipation. This appears to be the greatest disadvantage of the circuit. When thousands of switching circuits are used in a single piece of equipment, the current demand on the power supply is very high.

The calculations for the circuit shown in Figure 2-18 are very basic. The first step in a design is the selection of the Q point. Then the needed I_B is determined.

$$I_B = I_C/h_{FE}$$

R_B is then found by the following equation.

$$R_B = \frac{V_{CC} - V_{BE}}{I_B} \tag{2-24}$$

R_1 is simply an isolation resistor used to prevent the low resistance of the base circuit (when ON) from loading the pulse source.

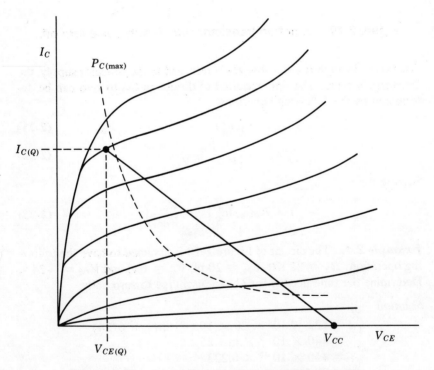

Figure 2-19.   Load line for circuit of Figure 2-18.

PROBLEMS

2.1. A certain PNP transistor is to be operated as a saturated switch. $V_{CC} = -35$ v, $I_{C(sat)} = 38$ ma, and $h_{FE(min)} = 18$. Calculate R_L and R_B. The input pulse varies from $+2$ to -6 v.

2.2. What is h_{FE} in the circuit of Figure 2-20?

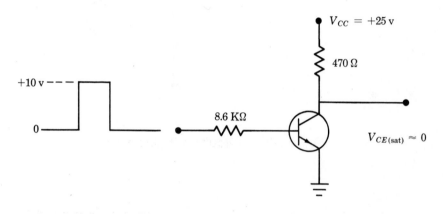

Figure 2-20.   Circuit for Problem 2.2.

2.3. A 2N2193 transistor is operated as a saturated switch in the circuit of Figure 2-21. The input pulse is rectangular and has a duration of 0.5 μsec. Sketch the output waveform.

2.4. For the circuit of Figure 2-22, calculate the rise time (a) when $V_{in} = -4.5$ v, and (b) when $V_{in} = -12$ v. $C_{eb} = 15$ pf and $V_{BE(sat)} = 1.3$ v.

2.5. A PNP transistor is to be operated as a saturated switch (Figure 2-6). $R_L = 680$ Ω, $V_{CC} = -18$ v, $V_{BB} = 3$ v, $h_{FE(min)} = 20$, $I_2 = 3$ ma, and $V_{in} = -6$ v. Calculate R_1 and R_B.

2.6. In the circuit of Figure 2-11, calculate I_D, given that $V_{CC} = 30$ v, $R_L = 1500$ Ω, $h_{FE} = 45$, $V_{CE(clamp)} = 1.2$ v, $V_{in} = 10$ v, and $R_1 = 15$ KΩ.

2.7. Given the circuit of Figure 2-23, calculate (a) I_B, (b) I_C, (c) R_1, and (d) R_2.

2.8. In the circuit of Figure 2-13 let $h_{FE} = 30$, $R_2 = 1800$ Ω, $V_{CC} = 20$ v, and $R_L = 1200$ Ω. What is the collector voltage at clamp?

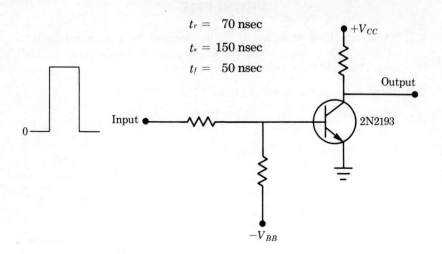

$t_r = $ 70 nsec

$t_s = $ 150 nsec

$t_f = $ 50 nsec

Figure 2-21. Circuit for Problem 2.3.

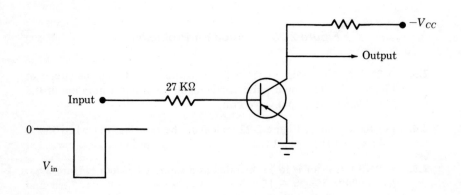

Figure 2-22. Circuit for Problem 2.4.

2.9. Given the circuit of Figure 2-24, solve for I_C and $V_{CE(\text{clamp})}$. Let $h_{FE(\text{min})} = 18$.

2.10. The circuit of Figure 2-25 is found to have a turn-OFF time of 75 nsec. Solve for the approximate value of C_{eb}.

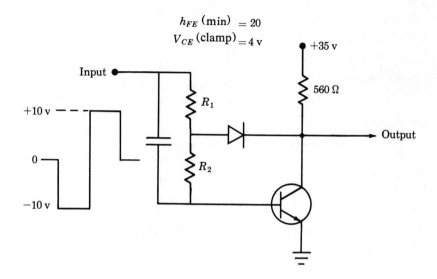

$$h_{FE} \, (\text{min}) = 20$$
$$V_{CE} \, (\text{clamp}) = 4 \, \text{v}$$

Figure 2-23. Circuit for Problem 2.7.

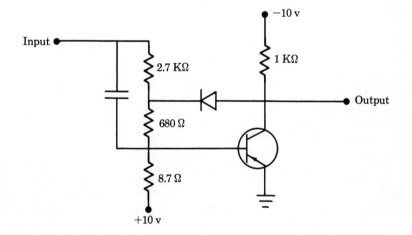

Figure 2-24. Circuit for Problem 2.9.

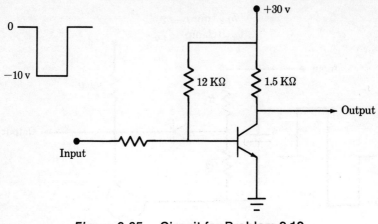

Figure 2-25.   Circuit for Problem 2.10.

CHAPTER 3

Semiconductor Logic Circuits

3-1 Introduction

This chapter will be devoted to the analysis of the various semiconductor logic gates. These gates are circuits that perform the Boolean algebraic operations discussed in Chapter 1.

Good functional design of a logic circuit requires the output of a logic circuit to switch between two definite voltage levels, rather than to change from point to point along some load line as the inputs to the gate are applied. In Chapter 1 it was pointed out that an OR gate will have a 1 output whenever one or more of the inputs is at 1. This then requires that we design circuits that will switch to the same voltage level regardless of the number of inputs applied to the OR gate. (There is one OR gate, the exclusive-OR, that operates only when just one input is at 1. If more than one input is at 1, the output of the exclusive-OR is 0).

Similarly, we learned that an AND gate cannot have a 1 ouput until all inputs are at 1. This means that there cannot be any change in output level until all inputs are present. The logic circuits designed along the lines discussed in these paragraphs are stable, and are less susceptible to noise and random signals.

41

3-2 OR Gates

Figure 3-1 illustrates a three-input diode OR gate. It should be apparent that whenever a positive pulse is applied to any of the inputs, there will be a positive pulse across the load resistance. To meet our requirements that the output voltage be the same regardless of the number of inputs present at any one time, R_L must be very much larger than the forward resistance of a diode. The circuit of Figure 3-1 can be arranged to operate as an OR gate when a negative pulse is defined as a 1 input. It is only necessary to turn the diodes around as in Figure 3-2.

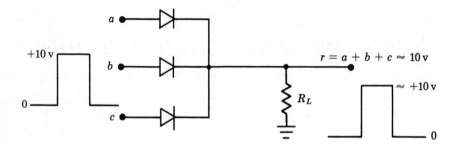

Figure 3-1.   Three-diode OR gate for positive inputs.

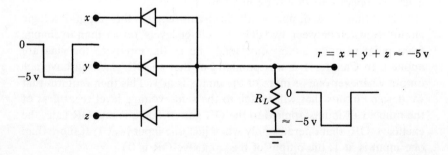

Figure 3-2.   Three-diode OR gate for negative inputs.

A very simple OR gate using a single transistor is shown in Figure 3-3. The circuit is essentially an emitter-follower that is in cutoff until an input pulse is applied to base of the transistor. Upon application of input the voltage across the load is in phase with the input pulse. The magnitude of voltage across the load will be approximately equal to V_{in}. The resistors R_1, R_2, and R_3 are used to isolate the pulse sources one from another. In order for the output to remain constant when more than one input is applied, R_L must be very much larger than the isolating resistors. This can make the output voltage temperature sensitive because of leakage current when the circuit is OFF.

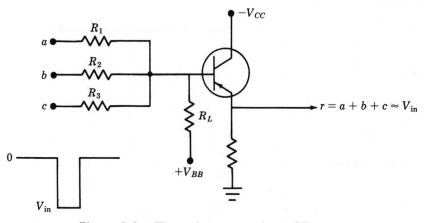

Figure 3-3.   Three-input transistor OR gate.

A circuit that avoids the need for large values of load resistance is shown in Figure 3-4. In this circuit, the isolation resistors have been re-placed by diodes. The very low forward resistance of a diode permits us

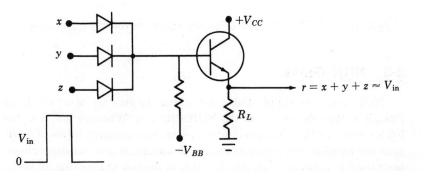

Figure 3-4.   Three-input OR gate using diode transistor logic.

to use a fairly low value of load resistance. Some sources will refer to this type of OR circuit as *diode-transistor* logic.

An effective OR gate can be made in which a transistor is used for each input. All emitters are connected in parallel to a common load resistor. This circuit provides complete isolation of input sources from each other. However, the cost of this circuit is the greatest of any of the OR circuits. This OR gate is shown in Figure 3-5.

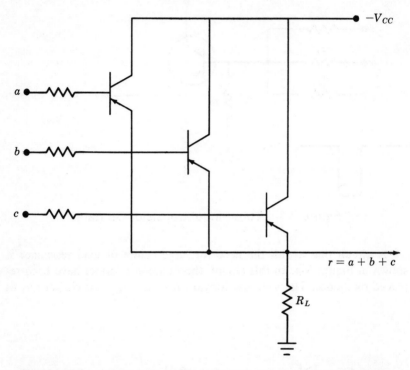

Figure 3-5. Three-input OR gate using separate transistors.

3-3 NOR Gates

NOR gates are simply OR gates whose outputs are inverted. If an input is 1, then the output of the NOR gate is 0. When all inputs to the NOR circuit are 0, then the output is 1. The most common forms of NOR gates are based on the common emitter arrangement of a transistor circuit since the CE amplifier is an inverter. It is of interest to note that all of the OR gates discussed in Section 3-2 were arranged as parallel switches. In this type of arrangement, a 1 must be defined as an input that "closes" a switch. When NOR gates are devised, a series arrangement as well as parallel arrangements are possible. When the semiconductor switches are connected in series, the NOR function is performed whenever an input is one that "opens" a switch.

Figure 3-6 is a common NOR circuit with the transistor operating into saturation. The analysis of the circuit is precisely the same as in Section 2-3. The base drive resistors again serve to isolate the pulse sources from one another. However, the size of R_L is not at all affected by these resistors. In the OR gate of Figure 3-3, we had an emitter-follower circuit whose output could never exceed the input, and a circuit in which the forward-biased base-to-emitter junction closed the path between the input and R_L. In the CE circuit of Figure 3-6, the voltage drop across R_L will be approximately V_{CC} so long as sufficient base current flows, regardless of the size of the base resistors in comparison to R_L.

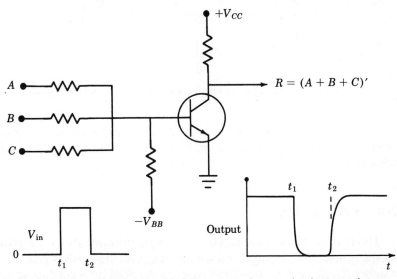

Figure 3-6. Three-input NOR gate using a single transistor.

The non-saturating techniques discussed in Section 2-5 can be applied to the circuit of Figure 3-6, permitting higher speed of operation. These same techniques are also readily applied to the circuit of Figure 3-7. This circuit is simply the CE version of Figure 3-5.

The circuit of Figure 3-8 makes use of the inputs to *turn off* the transistors. Since the units are in series, an input to either base will open the circuit and cause a new output. In the absence of input pulses the output

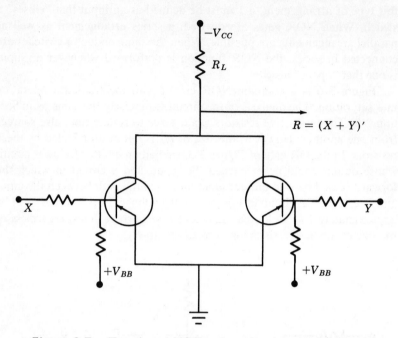

Figure 3-7. Two-input NOR gate using two transistors.

is approximately zero, since the resistors R_1 and R_2 forward bias the transistors and cause saturated operation. When an input is applied, the output becomes equal to V_{CC}.

3-4 AND Gates

Diode AND circuits are based on the basic principle that voltages in parallel cannot add. Figure 3-9 illustrates a typical diode AND gate. The resistors R_a, R_b, and R_c are shown to stress the need for a conductive return to ground that is considerably lower in resistance than the load resistance. Where the internal resistance of the input source is low compared to R_L, it is not necessary to use these resistors. The reader will note that all diodes are forward biased by the source voltage V_1.

The output is a low value of voltage approaching zero if R_L is a high resistance. Figure 3-10 shows the equivalent circuit with all diodes conducting. The output voltage when all diodes are conducting is found by Eq. (3-1).

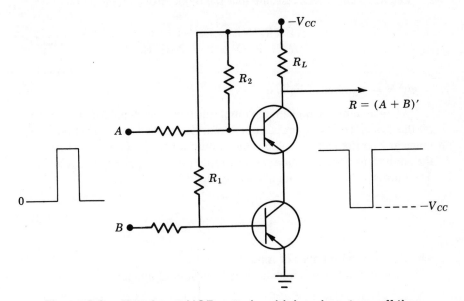

Figure 3-8. Two-input NOR gate in which pulses turn off the transistors.

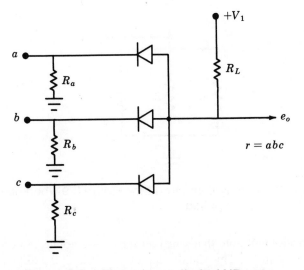

Figure 3-9. Three-input diode AND gate.

Let $R_a = R_b = R_c$. Assume that the diode drops are negligible:

$$e_o = \frac{V_1(R_a/N)}{R_L + R_a/N} = \frac{V_1}{1 + NR_L/R_a} \tag{3-1}$$

where N = number of inputs.

When an input is applied, the input must be of such polarity as to turn off the diode. To insure proper operation, the applied input must be very much greater than any possible value of output voltage. Figure 3-11 shows the equivalent circuit when a positive input pulse is applied to terminal a. The output voltage when inputs are applied is given by Eq. (3-2):

$$e_o = \frac{V_1}{1 + (N - x)R_L/R_a} \tag{3-2}$$

where N = total number of input terminals,
x = number of inputs to which pulses are applied.

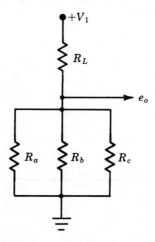

Figure 3-10.   Equivalent circuit for Figure 3-9 when no inputs are applied.

The reader will note that when all inputs are applied $(x = N)$, Eq. (3-2) reduces to V_1. This simply states that when all the diodes are back biased, the ouput is equal to the source voltage. Best operation of this particular AND circuit is obtained when the input pulses $\geq V_1$.

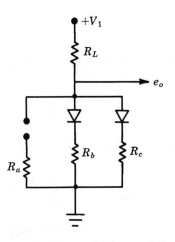

Figure 3-11.   The equivalent of Figure 3-9 with an input at
terminal *a*.

By the appropriate choice of a clamping voltage, it is possible to switch the diode AND gate to some voltage level that is different from both the input voltages and the source voltage. The operation of this circuit assumes that all inputs exceed V_1. Figure 3-12 shows the diode AND circuit with a 1 output clamped to V_R.

In this circuit, D_1 is back biased by V_R until all inputs are applied at the same time. When this occurs, the output tends to rise towards V_1. However, when the voltage at the anode of D_1 becomes slightly greater than V_R, then D_1 conducts and clamps the output at V_R. It should be apparent to the reader that the circuit cannot be clamped when $V_R \geq V_1$.

Another method of operating the diode AND gate is illustrated in Figure 3-13. In this case there is *always* an input voltage at each of the inputs. A 0 input to the gate is represented by a voltage that helps to forward bias the diode. A 1 input is a back-bias voltage to a diode. The output remains at a level equal to the 0 input, until all inputs are 1. Then the output switches to this level.

The operation of the circuit can be seen from the sketches of the pulse inputs in Figure 3-13. Prior to time t_1, all inputs are at $+6$ volts. All diodes are forward biased, and the output voltage is approximately $+6$ volts. At time t_1 the voltage at the X input switches to -6 volts. This back biases the diode in the X input line even though the source voltage may be many times larger than the 1 input at X. This is due to the fact

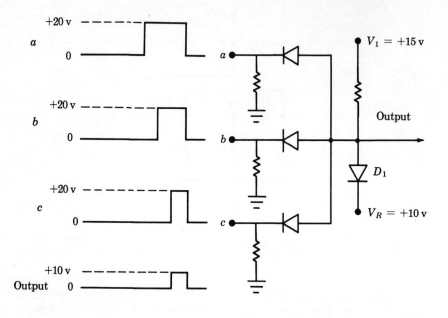

Figure 3-12. Three-input diode AND gate with a voltage clamp.

that the diodes in the Y and Z input lines are forward biased. The output therefore remains at slightly less than $+6$ volts.

At time t_2 both the X and Y inputs are at -6 volts. The diodes in these lines are now back biased. The output remains at approximately $+6$ volts. At time t_3 all inputs are at -6 volts. One again, *all* diodes are *forward biased*. The circuit behaves as if it had a source equal to $-[V_1 - 6]$. The output is now slightly less than -6 volts and is a 1. At time t_4 only the Z input is at -6 volts and the output returns to 0.

The transistor AND gate of Figure 3-14 is equivalent to an AND circuit made of parallel switches. For a parallel switch arrangement to function as an AND circuit, the inputs must open the switches. If we assume that the transistors are in saturation ($V_{CE} = 0$), then the output is equal to V_{CC}. When an input is applied so that a transistor is in cutoff, the output remains at V_{CC} because the other "switch" is still closed. When both inputs are applied and both transistors are in cutoff, the output volt-

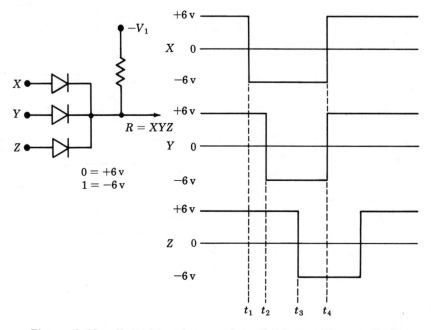

Figure 3-13. Example of operation of the three-input diode
AND gate.

age drops to zero. The resistors R_1 and R_2 are selected so as to forward
bias the transistors so that they are in saturation unless inputs are applied.

3-5 NAND Gates

Just as the transistor AND gate is usually arranged as an emitter-
follower circuit, the transistor NAND gate is a common emitter circuit.
The CE circuit offers voltage as well as current amplification, and also
inverts the output. Figure 3-15 is a NAND circuit that is similar to the
circuit of Figure 3-14. Again, the inputs must turn off the transistors.
Until both inputs are present, the output is approximately zero. When
both inputs are applied, the output is V_{CC}.

A series NAND gate can be arranged. In this case, the input pulses
turn on the circuit. The common emitter configuration is used with the
transistors connected in series as in Figure 3-16. The circuit requires as
many transistors as there are inputs. The parallel NAND circuit switched
from approximately 0 volts to V_{CC}. The series NAND circuit of Figure
3-16 switches from V_{CC} to approximately zero.

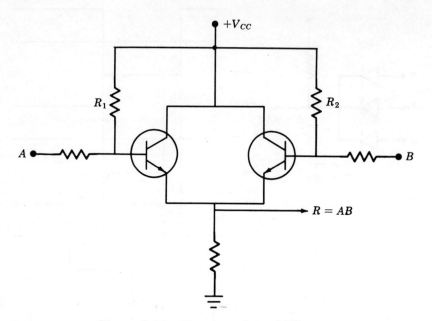

Figure 3-14.   Two-transistor AND gate.

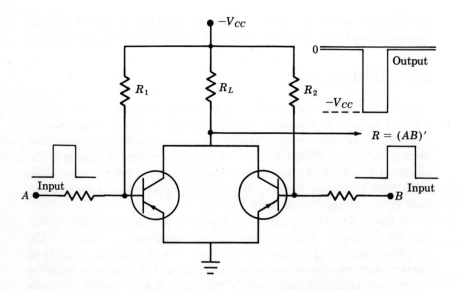

Figure 3-15.   Two-transistor NAND gate.

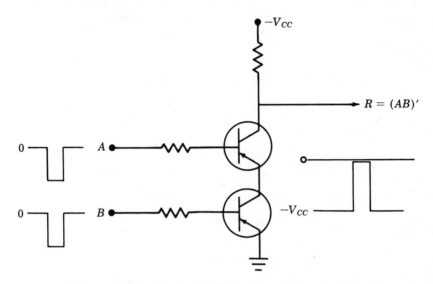

Figure 3-16. Series NAND gate with two inputs.

3-6 Applications of Logic Circuits

The reader will note that the NOR and NAND circuits discussed so far in this chapter were common emitter versions of OR and AND gates. It should be apparent that the CE circuit is used because of the inverting properties of this type of circuit. Any AND and OR circuit can be changed to a NAND and NOR gate simply by applying the output of the gate to a common emitter circuit.

The transistor logic circuits discussed in Sections 3-1 through 3-5 may be disadvantageous to use in practical systems because of the higher cost and greater complexity of these circuits as opposed to diode logic circuits. In most cases where inverted logic is needed, it may be more economical to use diode logic and inverter circuits than to use the transistor logic circuits. Transistor logic circuits do offer the advantage of less loading on the pulse source, and in cases where the pulse source has a high internal resistance, transistor logic can be used to advantage.

In this section, we will be concerned with the solution of Boolean algebra by means of the logic circuits discussed in the previous sections. We will solve these example problems by several different methods, and will also employ some of the theorems covered in Chapter 1.

Example 3.1. Devise several logic circuits based on the following equation (assume that the inputs are 15-volt positive pulses).

$$(A + B)C = R$$

Solution:

(a) Draw the block diagram of the problem.

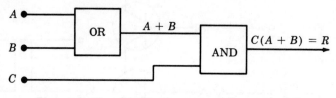

Figure 3-17. Block diagram of Example 3.1.

(b) Solution by use of diode logic.

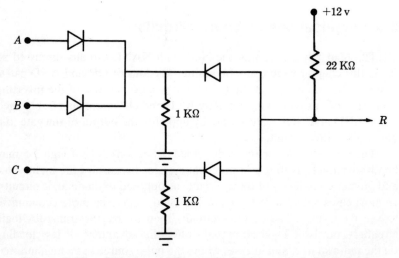

Figure 3-18. Solution to Example 3.1 by use of diode logic.

When none of the input pulses is present, the voltage at the output terminal is 267 mv. If any *one* input is applied, the output voltage changes to 521 mv. If pulses are applied only to the *A* and B terminals, the output remains at 521 mv. However, if a pulse is applied to C at the same time that pulses are applied to either A or B (or both), then the output becomes 12 volts.

(c) Figure 3-19 shows the solution of the equation by transistor logic.

When no inputs are applied, Q_1 and Q_2 are biased into saturation by resistors R_1 and R_2. The output voltage is equal to $-V_{CC}$. If only A or B inputs are applied, Q_1 becomes back biased. However, Q_2 remains in saturation and the output remains at approximately $-V_{CC}$. If only a C input is applied, Q_1 is in saturation while Q_2 is in cutoff, and the output remains at $-V_{CC}$. However, if there is an input at C while there is also input at A or B or both, then both transistors are in cutoff, and the output switches from $-V_{CC}$ to 0. It should be noted that the circuit was arranged to provide a positive pulse output at the R terminal. Since no inversion of the output is stated in the problem, and positive input is used, the output must also be positive.

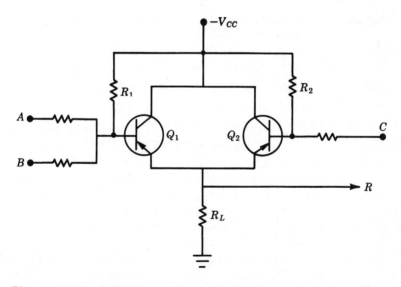

Figure 3-19. Solution to Example 3.1 by use of transistor logic.

(d) Solution by means of NOR logic.

(1) Expand the equation:

$$R = AC + BC$$

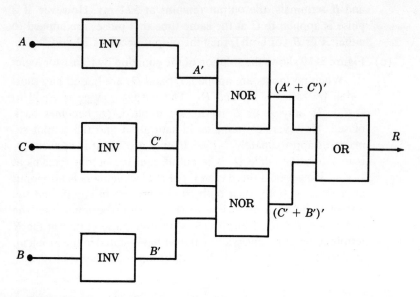

Figure 3-20.   Application of De Morgan's theorem to Example
          3.1.

(2) Apply De Morgan's theorem to the terms of the equation.
$$R = (A' + C')' + (B' + C')'$$

(3) Figure 3-20 is the block diagram of the circuit.

(4) Figure 3-21 is the solution of the equation by NOR logic.

The solution illustrated in Figure 3-21 is certainly complex and a much poorer solution to the problem than the
previous solutions. It has been included so that the reader
may get an insight into the problems involved when coupling
from one transistor logic circuit to another. It is also an
interesting demonstration of the theory and application of
De Morgan's theorem.

Assume that all inputs are 0. The inverters Q_1, Q_2, and
Q_3 are therefore in cutoff. The voltage at the collectors of
the transistors are approximately V_{CC}. The voltages are
coupled to the bases of the NOR gates (Q_4 and Q_5). These
transistors are in saturation as a result of the forward bias.
The collector voltages of Q_4 and Q_5 are approximately zero,
and the output at R is zero.

If an input is applied only at A, this inverter will go into
saturation, while the others are still in cutoff. The output

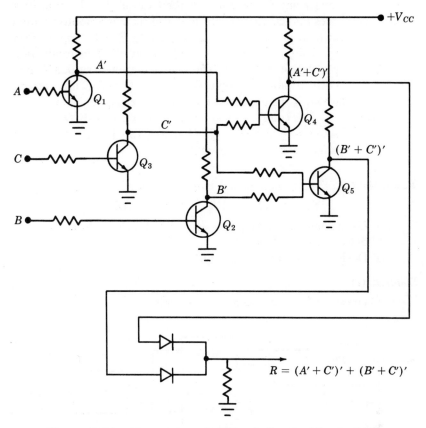

Figure 3-21. Transistor circuit solution to Figure 3-20.

from Q_1 can no longer forward bias Q_4, but the voltage available from Q_3 keeps Q_4 in saturation. Since no change has been made at the other inputs, Q_5 is also in saturation, and the resultant output of the entire circuit is still at zero.

If an input is applied only at B, then Q_2 goes into saturation; but Q_1 and Q_3 still drive the NOR gates into saturation, maintaining the output voltage of the system at zero.

When an input is applied only at C, driving Q_3 into saturation, Q_1 and Q_2 remain in cutoff. The NOR gates are still forward biased and remain in saturation, keeping the output at zero.

Assume that a pulse is applied to A and another to C.

Both Q_1 and Q_3 are driven into saturation. There is no longer any forward bias at the base of Q_4. This transistor goes into cutoff. $V_{CE} \pm V_{CC}$, and there is a positive output at R. If positive pulses are applied to B and C inputs, then Q_2 and Q_3 cut off, causing Q_5 to cut off. This results in a positive output at R. The reader will observe that R is a positive pulse any time B and C or A and C are present, which is the expanded form of the original equation.

The voltage $-V_{BB}$ in the base circuits of Q_4 and Q_5 is to insure that when Q_1, Q_2, and Q_3 are in saturation, there is a reverse bias on Q_4 and Q_5.

Example 3.2. The equations of a half-adder are:

$$\text{Sum} = AB' + A'B; \quad \text{Carry} = AB$$

   (i) Use a combination of diodes and transistors to perform the functions of a half-adder.
  (ii) Devise a half-adder using NOR logic.

Solution (i):

   (a) Draw the block diagram of the circuit.

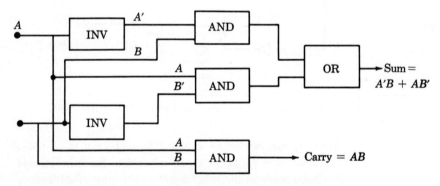

Figure 3-22.   Block diagram of half-adder.

   (b) Draw the circuit diagram based on the block diagram of Figure 3-22.
   (c) Test the circuit by means of a truth table.
       (1) When no inputs are present, the output from both gates must be 0. The voltages at the collectors of Q_1 and Q_2 both are equal to $+V_{CC}$ since both transistors are in cutoff.

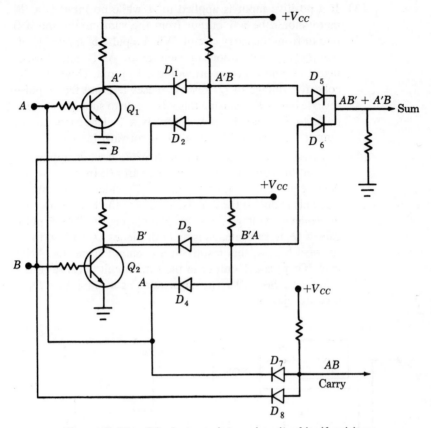

Figure 3-23.   Diode transistor circuit of half-adder.

Therefore diodes D_1 and D_3 are reverse biased. However diodes D_2 and D_4 are forward biased, and the voltage available to operate diodes D_5 and D_6 is very low. Therefore the output in the sum circuit is 0. The carry circuit also has a 0 output since D_7 and D_8 are forward biased.

(2) When positive pulses are present simultaneously at A and B, the carry circuit should have a 1 output, but the sum circuit must remain at 0. The input pulses reverse bias D_7 and D_8 resulting in 1 output. Diodes D_2 and D_4 are also reverse biased by the pulse inputs. However, both inverters are in saturation due to the input pulses, and D_1 and D_3 are forward biased causing 0 inputs to both terminals of the OR gate. The sum output remains at 0.

(3) If a positive input is applied to A while no input is at B, there should be a 1 output from the sum circuit and a 0 output from the carry circuit. When a pulse is applied to A, then Q_1 is in saturation, preventing the AND gate consisting of D_1 and D_2 from providing a 1 output. However, the collector voltage of Q_2 reverse biases D_3, and the A pulse reverse biases D_4, causing this AND gate to supply a positive pulse to D_6, and the sum output is a 1. The carry circuit output remains at 0 because D_8 is forward biased.

(4) If a positive pulse is applied to B while none is applied to A, then the sum must be 1 and the carry 0. In this case the AND gate consisting of D_1 and D_2 provides a 1 output to D_5. This is due to the B pulse reversing the bias on D_2 and the collector voltage of Q_1 reverse biasing D_1. The B pulse causes Q_2 to saturate, causing both diodes D_6 and D_4 to be forward biased; this results in a 0 output from this AND gate. There is a 1 output in the sum circuit because of the 1 input to diode D_5. The carry remains at 0 because D_7 is forward biased.

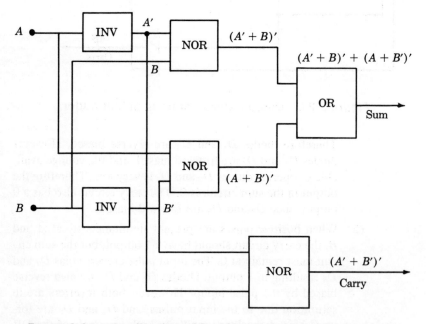

Figure 3-24.   Application of De Morgan's theorem to the half-adder circuit.

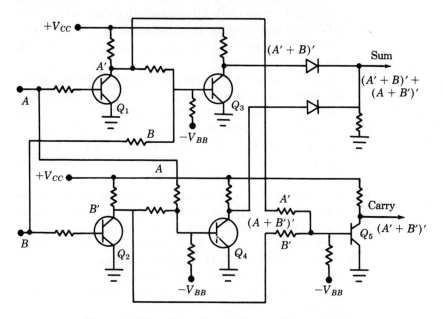

Figure 3-25.   Circuit solution to Figure 3-24.

The reader will note that the AND gates $D_1 - D_2$ and $D_3 - D_4$ followed the rules set down in Chapter 1. The inputs to the gates were all 1 inputs whenever the output was 1. There was no output whenever an input to the gate was 0. The input representing the *absence* of a pulse was provided by the use of inverters. Thus, when AB' was used to cause a 1 output, B' was 1 whenever B was 0. This is a repetition of a point made in the first chapter, but it is important enough to be repeated here.

Solution (ii):

    (a) Rewrite the equations using De Morgan's theorem.

$$\text{Sum} = (A' + B)' + (A + B')'$$
$$\text{Carry} = (A' + B')'$$

    (b) Sketch the block diagram.

    (c) Draw the circuit diagram based on the block diagram.

    (d) Test the circuit.

        (1) When both A and B are 0, the sum and carry outputs must be 0. If A is 0, then the collector voltage of Q_1 causes Q_3 to saturate, supplying a 0 to D_1. Similarly, the collector voltage

of Q_2 forward biases Q_4, causing a 0 input to D_2. Because both inputs to the diode OR gate are 0, the output is 0. The NOR gate that supplies the carry output (Q_5) is in saturation due to inputs from both Q_1 and Q_2; therefore, the output is 0.

(2) When both A and B inputs are at 1, there should be a 0 from the sum circuit and a 1 from the carry circuit. Inverters Q_1 and Q_2 are in saturation. Q_5 is therefore in cutoff, and the output from the carry is 1 and equal to V_{CC}. The A pulse causes the output of Q_4 to be 0, while the B pulse causes the output of Q_3 to be 0. Therefore the carry is 1 and the sum is 0.

(3) If A is 1 while B is 0, the carry output must be 0 and the sum output is 1. The A input causes inverter Q_1 to supply a 0 to Q_3 at the instant that there is no other input to Q_3. With both inputs of this NOR gate at 0, the output to the diode OR gate is a 1. Q_2 supplies 1 inputs to Q_4 and Q_5, causing these NOR gates to have 0 outputs. Since there is a 1 input to the diode OR gate, the sum output is 1 while the carry is 0.

(4) If B is 1 while A is 0, the sum must be 1 and the carry must be 0. Q_2 supplies the only input to Q_4 at this time. Since B is a 1, the output of Q_2 is a 0. This 0 input to the Q_4 NOR gate supplies a 1 input to the diode OR gate. The carry circuit still provides a 0 output because Q_1 provides a 1 input to Q_5.

PROBLEMS

3.1. Sketch the diagram of a NAND gate that includes collector voltage clamping in order to increase operating speed.

3.2. Turning off a transistor, rather than turning it on reduces the time required to switch the transistor as compared to a saturated switch. Design an OR gate with inputs that turn it OFF rather than ON.

3.3. The circuit of Figure 3-26 is a diode logic system. Write the equation of the circuit, and specify the output voltages for 0 and 1.

3.4. Sketch a diode logic circuit for the following equation.
$$(A + B)\,(CD) = R$$

3.5. Design a transistor logic circuit for the circuit shown in Figure 1-7.

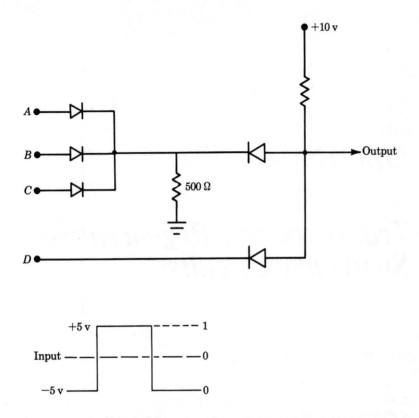

Figure 3-26. Circuit for Problem 3.3.

3.6. A diode logic circuit is based upon the following equation:
$$A[(XY)' + BY] = R$$
(a) Sketch the logic circuit.
(b) Redraw the circuit using transistors, and replace all AND gates with NOR logic by use of De Morgan's theorem.

3.7. By use of logic circuits and a truth table, prove that
$$(ABC)' = A' + B' + C'$$

3.8. Use logic circuits and a truth table to prove that
$$A + A'C = A + C$$

3.9. Sketch the circuits of the half-adder using non-saturated transistor switching circuits for the logic gates.

3.10. What might be a reason to limit the number of inputs to a diode AND gate?

CHAPTER 4

Transistorized Regenerative Switching Circuits

4-1 Introduction

In this chapter we shall discuss the various forms of bistable, mono-stable, and astable transistor switching circuits. These are various types of multivibrators, blocking oscillators, and Schmitt triggers. We shall also discuss the methods of triggering the circuits.

An astable circuit has no stable states. It is a regenerative switching circuit that constantly changes from one state to another, without any external input pulses required to cause switching. In short, it is an oscillating circuit.

A monostable circuit has one stable state and one quasi-stable state. The circuit remains in its stable state until an input trigger pulse is applied. It then switches to the semi-stable state, and after some period of time it reverts back to the stable state. Only one input pulse is needed to complete a cycle of operation of the circuit: from stable state to quasi-stable, and back to stable state.

A bistable circuit has two stable states. Upon the application of an input pulse, the circuit switches from one stable state to the other. Another pulse is required to complete the cycle of operation, causing the circuit to return to its original state.

In *all* regenerative transistor switching circuits, the switching action takes place from within the cutoff region to either saturation or to some clamped level.

4-2   Astable Multivibrators

Most multivibrators are regenerative-coupled CE amplifiers. The circuit of Figure 4-1 is the schematic diagram of an astable multivibrator. The output waveform is shown at the collector of Q_2. A similar waveform, but 180° out of phase, is available at the collector of Q_1.

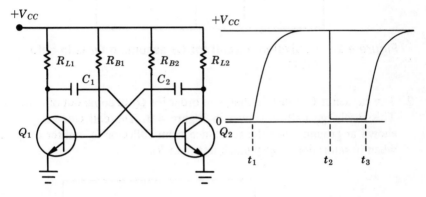

Figure 4-1.   Astable multivibrator and collector waveform.

The operation of any regenerative switching circuit is most clearly understood if we assume proper operation of the circuit, and then proceed with explanations of the operation.

1. To begin our discussion, assume that Q_1 is in cutoff and that Q_2 is in saturation. At this instant, the operating potentials around the circuit are:

$$V_{BE1} = \text{some negative voltage} \qquad V_{BE2} = 300 \text{ mv}$$
$$V_{CE1} = V_{CC} \qquad\qquad\qquad\quad V_{CE2} = 0$$
$$e_{C1} = V_{CC} \qquad\qquad\qquad\quad\ e_{C2} = V_{BE1}$$

The equivalent circuit of the multivibrator when Q_1 is in cutoff and Q_2 is in saturation is shown in Figure 4-2. For all practical purposes the capacitor C_1 is in series with R_{L1} across the collector voltage supply, and C_2 is effectively between base and ground of Q_1. (Q_2 is ignored since $V_{BE(\text{sat})}$ and $V_{CE(\text{sat})}$ are very small.)

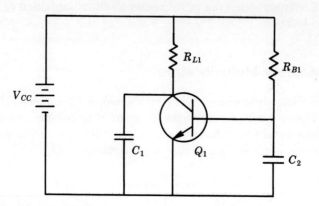

Figure 4-2.   Equivalent circuit for Q_1 assuming Q_2 is in saturation.

2. The capacitor C_2 must discharge in order for Q_1 to come out of cutoff. This discharge path is shown in Figure 4-3. The collector of Q_2 is shown at ground since the resistance from collector to emitter of Q_2 when in saturation is very much less than R_{B1}.

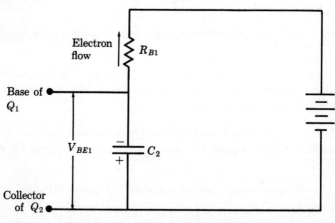

Figure 4-3.   Discharge path for C_2.

3. At the time that V_{BE1} becomes just slightly greater than zero, Q_1 will start to turn on. V_{CE1} therefore drops. Since C_1 cannot change charge instantaneously, this drop in V_{CE1} is immediately coupled to the base of Q_2, driving Q_2 into cutoff. With Q_2 in cutoff, V_{CE2} starts to rise to-

wards V_{CC}. This rise is coupled to the base of Q_1, driving it into saturation. C_2 now charges through the emitter-base junction of Q_1 and the
load resistor R_{L2}. The charge path is shown in Figure 4-4. The reader
will recall that while Q_1 was in cutoff, C_2 was effectively connected between base and emitter of Q_1. When Q_1 is in saturation and Q_2 is in
cutoff, C_2 is connected between the base of Q_1 and the collector of Q_2.

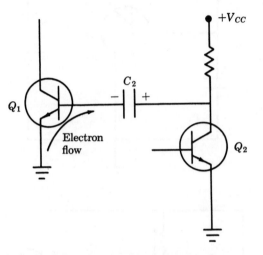

Figure 4-4.   Charge path for C_2.

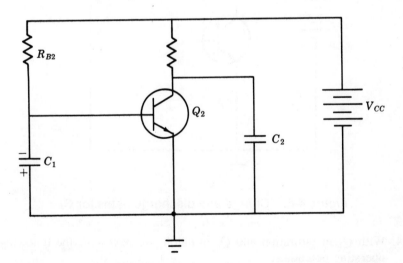

Figure 4-5.   Equivalent circuit for Q_2 when Q_1 is in saturation.

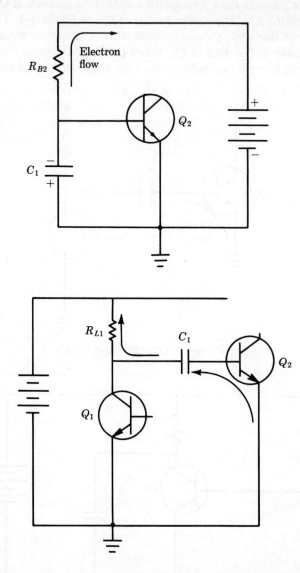

Figure 4-6. Charge and discharge paths for C_1.

4. With Q_1 in saturation and Q_2 in cutoff, we now have the following operating potentials:

$$V_{BE1} \cong 300 \text{ mv} \qquad V_{BE2} = \text{some negative voltage}$$
$$V_{CE1} \cong 0 \qquad\qquad V_{CE2} = V_{CC}$$
$$e_{C1} = V_{BE2} \qquad\quad e_{C2} = V_{CC}$$

Figure 4-5 is the equivalent circuit for this mode of operation.

5. Instantly upon Q_1 saturating, C_1 is effectively connected between the base and emitter of Q_2, back-biasing the emitter junction by an amount equal to $-V_{CC}$. Now, C_1 begins to discharge through R_{B2}. When the voltage across C_1 is positive and just slightly greater than zero, Q_2 will begin to conduct. V_{CE2} drops, causing the base of Q_1 to go negative. This drives Q_1 into cutoff, causing V_{CE1} to rise. This rise is coupled to the base of Q_2, driving Q_2 into saturation. V_{CE1} does not instantly rise to V_{CC} because C_1 is now charging through the emitter and base of Q_2 and R_{L1}. When the charge on C_1 is equal to $V_{CC} - V_{BE2(sat)}$, current flow through R_{L1} stops and V_{CE} is equal to V_{CC}. Figure 4-6(a) shows the discharge path for C_1, and Figure 4-6(b) shows the charge path for C_1.

It is now of interest to examine all of the waveshapes of voltage at the various terminals (Figure 4-7). The waveforms start with the assuméd conditions used in part (a) of our discussion of the operation of the multivibrator.

The time interval from t_1 to t_3 in Figure 4-7 is one cycle of operation of the astable multivibrator. The time from t_1 to t_2 is controlled by C_1 and R_{B2}, and the time from t_2 to t_3 is controlled by C_2 and R_{B1}. The intervals shown in the collector waveshapes τ_1 and τ_2 are controlled by $C_1 R_{L1}$ and $C_2 R_{L2}$. A fairly precise determination of the time intervals $t_1 - t_2$ and $t_2 - t_3$ may be calculated by use of the circuit of Figure 4-8.

At the instant of a transition such as at the time t_1, C_1 is charged to approximately V_{CC}. So far in our discussion, we have said that C_1 discharges. This was done for the sake of simplicity in the discussion. In actuality, C_1 as shown in Figure 4-8 would charge to V_{CC}. However, the point from which C_1 starts to "charge" is $-V_{CC}$. When the charge on C_1 is approximately equal to 0, then Q_2 will begin to conduct. Applying the standard equation for the charge of a capacitor, we have:

$$0 = 2V_{CC}(1 - \epsilon^{-t/RC}) - V_{CC}$$
$$\frac{V_{CC}}{2V_{CC}} = (1 - \epsilon^{-t/RC})$$
$$0.5 = \epsilon^{-t/RC}$$
$$t/RC = 0.69$$
$$t = 0.69 C_1 R_{B2} = T_A \qquad\qquad \textbf{(4-1)}$$

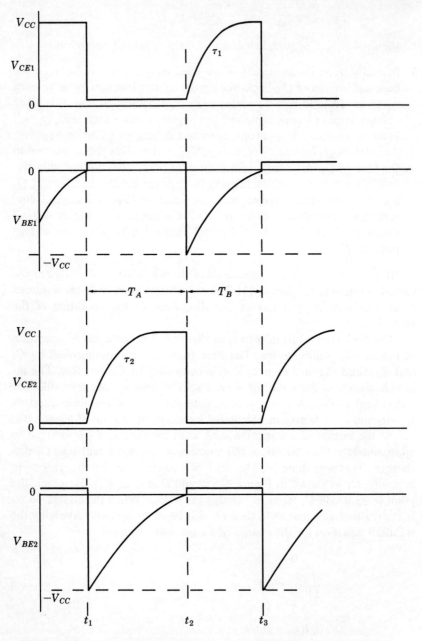

Figure 4-7. Base and collector waveforms for the astable multivibrator.

The interval T_A is found in the same manner.

$$T_B = 0.69C_2R_{B1} \qquad \textbf{(4-2)}$$

The frequency of oscillation of the multivibrator is then found.

$$F = \frac{1}{T_A + T_B} \qquad \textbf{(4-3)}$$

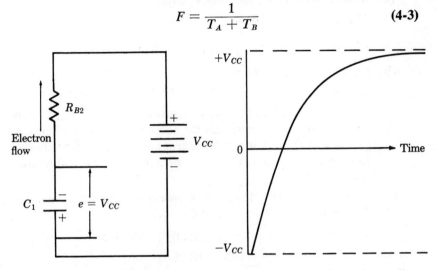

Figure 4-8. Equivalent circuit for the calculation of cutoff time for Q_2.

The astable multivibrator will be reliable if the following design criteria are met.

1. The base current must be sufficiently high to insure saturation.

$$R_{B1} = R_{B2} < \frac{V_{CC}h_{FE(min)}}{I_{C(sat)}} \qquad \textbf{(4-4)}$$

Since $I_{C(sat)} = V_{CC}/R_L$, then

$$R_{B1} = R_{B2} < hF_{FE(min)}R_L \qquad \textbf{(4-5)}$$

2. R_{B1} and R_{B2} must be much greater than the input resistance when the transistor is in saturation.

3. R_{B1} and R_{B2} must be much less than the input resistance when the transistor is in cutoff.

4. The time constants $R_{L1}C_1$ and $R_{L2}C_2$ must be much less than the base circuit time constants $R_{B1}C_2$ and $R_{B2}C_1$. This is so that the capacitors C_1 and C_2 will recharge quickly during off periods.

Example 4.1. Type 2N1198 transistors are to be used in an astable multivibrator. The circuit shall be symmetrical and have a frequency of 2,590 cps. Given that $h_{FE(min)} = 17$, $I_{C(max)} = 75$ ma, $V_{CE(max)} = 25$ v, and the collector supply $= +18$ v.

Solution:

(a) Select a value of R_L such that $I_{C(sat)} < I_{C(max)}$.

   (1) Let $I_{C(sat)} = 50$ ma.

   (2) $R_L = \dfrac{V_{CC}}{I_{C(sat)}} = \dfrac{18}{50 \times 10^{-3}} = 360 \ \Omega$

(b) Calculate R_B. [Eq. (4-5)]

   $R_{B1} = R_{B2}$ $\qquad$ $h_{FE(min)} R_L = 17 \times 360 = 6120 \ \Omega$

   To insure sufficient drive to saturate, let $R_{B1} = R_{B2} = 5.6$ KΩ. The reader will note that the collector current is a function of V_{CC} and R_L, and is not dependent upon a particular value of I$_B$ *so long as* I$_B$ *is great enough to drive the transistor into saturation.*

(c) Calculate C_1 and C_2. The problem specifies a symmetrical output. Therefore, $T_A = T_B = T$ and $C_1 = C_2$.

$$T_A = T_B = 1/2F = 1/1580 = 193 \ \mu sec$$

$$C = \frac{T}{0.69 \ R_B} = \frac{193 \times 10^{-6}}{0.69 \times 5.6 \times 10^3} = 50 \times 10^{-9}$$

$$C_1 = C_2 = 0.05 \ \mu fd$$

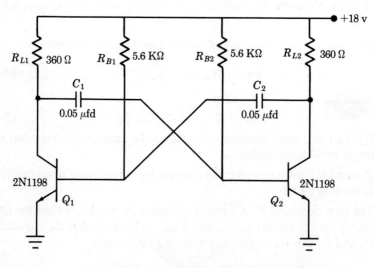

Figure 4-9. Circuit for Example 4.1.

(d) Check the time constant $R_L C$.

$$R_L C = 360 \times 50 \times 10^{-9} = 18 \ \mu sec$$

Since this time constant is much less than T_A or T_B, we are assured that C_1 and C_2 will quickly charge to V_{CC} during OFF periods for Q_1 and Q_2.

(e) Draw the circuit diagram.

Example 4.2. Type 2N1057 transistors are to be used in an astable multivibrator. The output must have the waveshape shown in Figure 4-10. $V_{CE(max)} = -45$ v, $I_{C(max)} = 300$ ma, and $h_{FE(min)} = 34$.

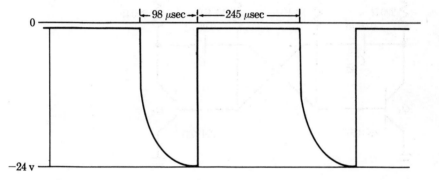

Figure 4-10. Waveform for the multivibrator of Example 4.2.

Solution:

(a) Let $I_{C(sat)} = 110$ ma.

(b) $R_L = \dfrac{V_{CC}}{I_{C(sat)}} = 220 \ \Omega$

(c) $R_B = h_{FE(min)} R_L = 34 \times 220 = 7400 \ \Omega$

   Let $R_{B1} = R_{B2} = 7.1$ KΩ

(d) During the interval T_1, Q_2 is in cutoff. This time is determined by $C_1 R_{B2}$. Solve for C_1.

$$C_1 = \frac{T_1}{0.69 \ R_{B2}} = \frac{98 \times 10^{-6}}{0.69 \times 7.1 \times 10^3} = 0.02 \ \mu fd$$

(e) The interval T_2 is the period for which Q_1 is in cutoff. This is determined by $R_{B1} C_2$. Solve for C_2.

$$C_2 = \frac{T_2}{0.69 \ R_{B1}} = \frac{245 \times 10^{-6}}{0.69 \times 7.1 \times 10^3} = 50 \times 10^{-9} = 0.05 \ \mu fd$$

(f) Check the recharging times for C_1 and C_2.

(1) $C_2 R_{L2} = 50 \times 10^{-9} \times 220 = 11 \ \mu\text{sec}$

This time constant is much less than 98 μsec, and therefore is satisfactory.

(2) $C_1 R_{L1} = 20 \times 10^{-9} \times 220 = 4.4 \ \mu\text{sec}$

This time constant is much less than 245 μsec, and therefore C_1 quickly recharges to $-V_{CC}$.

(g) Draw the diagram of the circuit. (Figure 4-11)

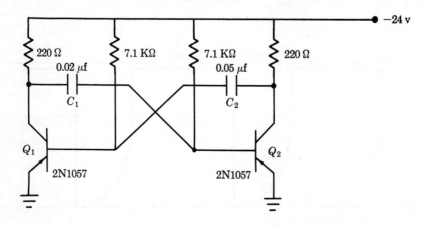

Figure 4-11. The circuit for Example 4.2.

4-3 Monostable Multivibrators

Monostable circuits are used either to generate time delay between pulses or to standardize pulses of random widths. Time delay is obtained by using the circuit to provide a trigger pulse output at some prescribed time interval after the application of a pulse input to the circuit. When the monostable is used to standardize pulses of random widths, the random pulses are first shaped into appropriate trigger inputs to the monostable circuit. The circuit provides an output pulse for each input pulse. Since the output pulses are identical, the circuit has thus been used to reshape pulses that have been degraded by other circuits, or pulses with non-uniform widths and to change these into pulses of uniform amplitude and width.

Figure 4-12 is the circuit diagram of a collector-coupled monostable multivibrator.

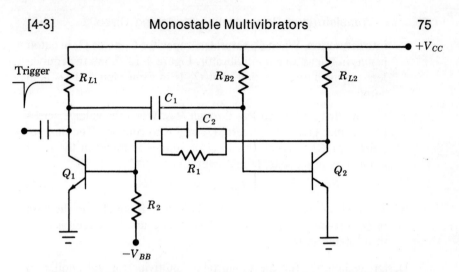

Figure 4-12. Collector-coupled monostable multivibrator.

THEORY OF OPERATION:

a. In the stable state, Q_1 is in cutoff and Q_2 is in saturation.

$$V_{CE1} = V_{CC} \qquad V_{CE2} \cong 0$$

$$V_{BE1} = \frac{-V_{BB}R_1}{R_1 + R_2} \qquad V_{BE2} \cong 300 \text{ mv}$$

$$I_{C1} = 0$$
$$e_{C1} = V_{CC} \qquad I_{C2} = \frac{V_{CC}}{R_{L2}}$$

b. When a negative trigger pulse is applied as shown in Figure 4-12, Q_2 cuts off. V_{CE2} rises and forward biases Q_1, causing Q_1 to go

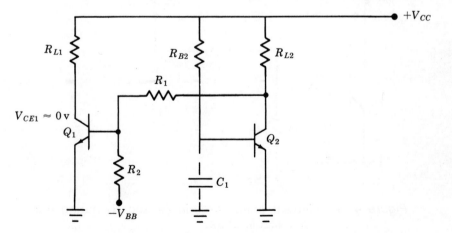

Figure 4-13. Equivalent circuit during the quasi-stable state.

into saturation. When Q_1 saturates, capacitor C_1 holds Q_2 in cutoff just as in the astable multivibrator. Figure 4-13 shows the equivalent circuit during the time that Q_1 is in saturation and Q_2 is in cutoff.

c. C_1 now charges toward V_{CC} through R_{B2}. When the voltage across C_1 becomes greater than zero, Q_2 begins to conduct. The time required for C_1 to reach this level of voltage is found in the same manner as in the astable multivibrator.

$$T = 0.69\ C_1 R_{B2} \qquad\qquad \textbf{(4-1)}$$

d. When Q_2 comes on, V_{CE2} drops. This drop is coupled to the base of Q_1, driving Q_1 into cutoff. When this occurs, the circuit is back in its stable state.

Design techniques for the monostable multivibrator are similar to those for the astable multivibrator. This is particularly so for calculations of R_{L1}, R_{L2}, C_1, and R_{B2}. However, the coupling network consisting of R_1 and R_2 must be carefully selected so that there is sufficient forward bias on Q_1 when the circuit is in the quasi-stable state. Figure 4-14 shows the equivalent circuit of the monostable multivibrator when in the quasi-stable state.

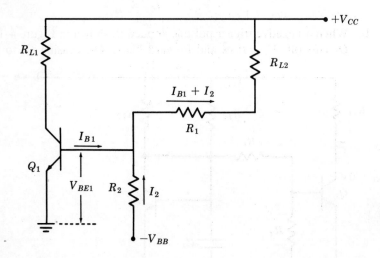

Figure 4-14. Current paths through R_1 and R_2 during the quasi-stable state.

The first step in the selection of R_1 and R_2 is the computation of I_B.

$$I_{B1} > \frac{V_{CC}}{R_{L1}h_{FE(\min)}} \qquad (4\text{-}6)$$

After calculating I_{B1}, select I_2 so that it is considerably less than I_{B1}. This is done to keep the drop across R_{L2} as small as possible.

R_2 is then readily calculated.

$$R_2 = \frac{|V_{BB}| + |V_{BE1}|}{I_2} \qquad (4\text{-}7)$$

R_1 is then found.

$$R_1 = \frac{|V_{CC}| - |V_{BE1}|}{I_{B1} + I_2} - R_{L2} \qquad (4\text{-}8)$$

Example 4.3.   A monostable multivibrator is to be used to develop a negative pulse output 141 μsec after the application of a trigger pulse. Type 2N1198 transistors are to be used. Given that $h_{FE(\min)} = 17$, $I_{C(\max)} = 75$ ma, and $V_{CE(\max)} = 25$ v. The circuit is to be used with a collector source of 18 v, and a base bias source of -1.5 v.

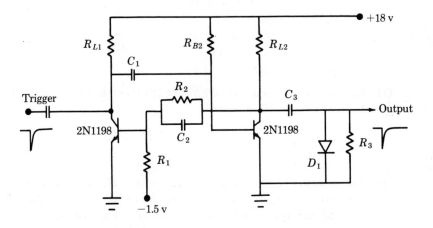

Figure 4-15.   Circuit for Example 4.3.

Solution:

(a) Draw the schematic diagram of the circuit. (Figure 4-15)

(b) Select a value of R_L such that $I_{C(\text{sat})} < I_{C(\max)}$.

(1) Let $I_{C(\text{sat})} = 60$ ma.

(2) $R_L = \dfrac{V_{CC}}{I_{C(\text{sat})}} = 300 \ \Omega$

$$R_{L1} = R_{L2} = 300 \ \Omega$$

(c) Calculate R_{B2} by use of Eq. (4-5).

$$R_{B2} \leq h_{FE(\text{min})} R_L = 17 \times 300 = 5.1 \ \text{K}\Omega$$

(d) Calculate C_1 by means of Eq. (4-1).

$$C_1 = \dfrac{T}{0.69 \ R_{B2}} = \dfrac{141 \times 10^{-6}}{0.69 \times 5.1 \times 10^3} = 0.04 \ \mu\text{fd}$$

(e) Calculate I_{B1} by use of Eq. (4-6).

$$I_{B1} \geq \dfrac{18}{300 \times 17} = 3.53 \ \text{ma}$$

(f) Let $I_2 = 0.1 \ I_{B1}$

$$I_2 = 0.353 \ \text{ma}$$

(g) Calculate R_2 by means of Eq. (4-7). (Assume that $V_{BE(\text{sat})} = 300$ mv.)

$$R_2 = \dfrac{1.5 + 0.3}{0.353 \times 10^{-3}} = 5.1 \ \text{K}\Omega$$

(h) Calculate R_1 by means of Eq. (4-8).

$$R_1 = \dfrac{18 - 0.3}{(3.53 + 0.353) \times 10^{-3}} - 300$$
$$= 4.26 \ \text{K}\Omega$$

(i) Calculate C_2. C_2 is a "speed-up" capacitor and is simply selected so that $R_1 C_2 = 10^{-6}$ seconds.

$$C_2 = \dfrac{10^{-6}}{R_1} = \dfrac{10^{-6}}{0.426 \times 10^4} = 2.35 \times 10^{-10}$$
$$= 235 \ \text{pf}$$

(j) The waveshaping network consisting of C_3, D_1, and R_3 is used to change the output waveform of the circuit into a negative pulse. In order to explain clearly the operation of the shaping circuit, let us examine the waveform available at the collector of Q_2.

When the circuit is in its stable state, Q_2 is in saturation and $V_{CE2} = 0$. When a trigger pulse is applied, Q_2 is driven into cutoff and V_{CE2} rises to V_{CC}. The voltage at the collector of Q_2 remains at V_{CC} for the period of the quasi-stable state (in this case, 141 μsec). When Q_2 comes out of cutoff, it is driven into saturation, and V_{CE2} again drops to approximately zero. Figure 4-16 shows the waveform at the collector of Q_2.

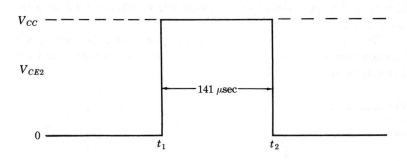

Figure 4-16.   Output waveform at collector of Q_2.

Now let us consider the application of this waveform to C_3, R_3, and D_1. (Figure 4-17)

At time t_1, the input rises from 0 to V_{CC}. Since C_3 cannot charge instantaneously, this voltage is dropped across R_{L2} and the parallel combination of D_1 and R_3. If we assume that the forward resistance of D_1 is much less than R_{L2} and that R_3 is much larger than R_{L2}, then for all practical purposes there is very little voltage developed across the combination of D_1 and R_3. Capacitor C_3 quickly charges to $+V_{CC}$ after time t_1. At the instant t_2, Q_2 is in saturation and effectively shorts the positively charged side of C_3 to ground. The diode D_1 is back biased by the charge on C_3, and C_3 quickly discharges through R_3 and Q_2.

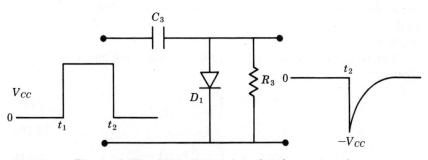

Figure 4-17.   Negative pulse shaping network.

The circuit is essentially an R-C differentiating network. The purpose of D_1 is to eliminate the positive spike that would normally be obtained in the output of a differentiating circuit. The wave-shaping circuit is not at all critical in design. It is only necessary that $R_3C_3 \ll t_2 - t_1$. Figure 4-18 illustrates the operation of the multivibrator of Example 4.3 as a time-delay circuit.

The reader will observe that the output pulses have the same spacings between them as do the input pulses. However, each output pulse follows a trigger pulse by 141 microseconds.

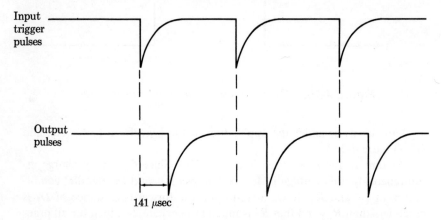

Figure 4-18.   Delayed pulse output from monostable multivibrator.

A self-biased monostable multivibrator is shown in Figure 4-19. In the stable state, the drop across R_3 causes Q_1 to be in cutoff. Q_2 is in saturation because of the forward bias through R_{B2}. In the figure PNP transistors are used, and a positive pulse to the base of the ON unit (collector of the OFF unit) is used to cause transition from the stable to the semi-stable state.

The equations for the various voltages around the circuit are easily written.

$$V_E = V_{CC}\left(\frac{R_3}{R_{L2} + R_3}\right) \tag{4-9}$$

$$V_{C2} = V_E + V_{CE2(\text{sat})} \tag{4-10}$$

$$V_{B1} = V_{C2}\left(\frac{R_2}{R_1 + R_2}\right) \tag{4-11}$$

The emitter junction of Q_1 will remain reverse biased so long as V_{B1} is less than V_E.

In the stable state, Q_1 is in cutoff and Q_2 is in saturation. Because the

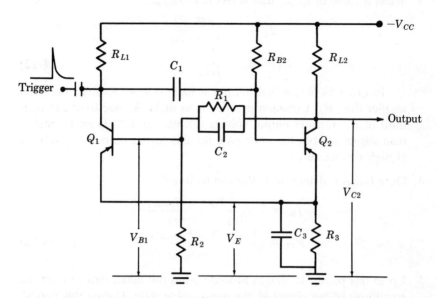

Figure 4-19.   Self-biased monostable multivibrator.

voltage V_E is greater than V_{B1}, the circuit remains in its stable state until a trigger pulse is applied. The trigger causes Q_2 to cut off. When Q_2 cuts off V_{C2} rises to $V_{CC} - V_E$ and drives Q_1 into saturation. When Q_1 saturates, the capacitor C_1 is effectively connected between base and emitter of Q_2. Prior to the transition, C_1 was charged to $V_{CC} - V_E$. After the transition, C_1 appears between base and emitter of Q_2 so that the positively charged side of C_1 is at the base of Q_2. This causes Q_2 to remain reverse biased until the charge on C_1 drops to zero as C_1 charges towards $V_{CC} - V_E$ through R_{B2}. The timing of the quasi-stable state is precisely as in the astable multivibrator and as in the collector-coupled monostable.

Design procedures for the self-biased monostable multivibrator differ appreciably from the collector-coupled unit. The following procedure is based upon using the same operating conditions for Q_1 and Q_2.

1. Let $R_{L1} = R_{L2}$. This will cause $I_{C(sat)}$ for each transistor to be the same.

2. To make most efficient use of the supply voltage, V_E must be much smaller than V_{CC}. The voltage V_E subtracts from the useful output. However, if V_E is made too small, the circuit will become unstable at high temperatures due to changes in $V_{CE(sat)}$ and h_{FE}.

3. Select a value of $I_{C(\text{sat})}$ that is less than $I_{C(\text{max})}$.

$$I_{C(\text{sat})} = \frac{V_{CC}}{R_L + R_3}$$

$$R_L + R_3 = \frac{V_{CC}}{I_{C(\text{sat})}} \tag{4-12}$$

In order to obtain high output voltage swings, R_3 must be much smaller than R_L. Common practice is to make R_3 one-fourth to one-third of R_L. Greater output voltage is obtained if R_3 is made smaller than suggested, but the price paid for this higher output is instability at high temperatures.

4. Once $I_{C(\text{sat})}$ is determined, R_{B2} can be found.

$$I_{B2} = \frac{V_{CC} - V_E}{R_{B2}} = \frac{I_{C(\text{sat})}}{h_{FE(\text{min})}}$$

$$R_{B2} = \frac{(V_{CC} - V_E)h_{FE(\text{min})}}{I_{C(\text{sat})}} \tag{4-13}$$

5. Up to this point, the design procedure has not taken into account the conditions of the circuit in the quasi-stable state. During this period, Q_1 is forward biased, and V_{B1} is approximately equal to V_E. Also, V_{C1} is approximately equal to V_E.

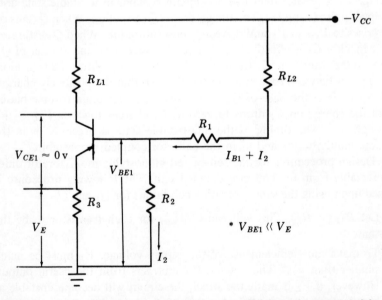

Figure 4-20. Equivalent circuit of self-biased monostable multivibrator during quasi-stable state.

6. C_1 and R_{B2} determine the duration of the quasi-stable period.

$$T = 0.69 \, R_{B2}C_1$$

$$C_1 = \frac{T}{0.69 \, R_{B2}} \qquad \text{(4-1)}$$

7. Figure 4-20 illustrates the equivalent circuit of the monostable multivibrator during the quasi-stable state. It is from this circuit that we shall calculate R_1 and R_2.

a. I_{B1} is known, since it is equal to I_{B2}.

b. Let $I_2 = 0.1 \, I_{B1}$.

c. $R_2 = \dfrac{V_E}{I_2}$ \qquad\qquad\qquad\qquad\qquad\qquad (4-14)

d. $R_1 = \dfrac{V_{CC} - V_E}{I_{B1} + I_2}$ \qquad\qquad\qquad\qquad\qquad (4-15)

8. Capacitor C_2 is simply selected so that $C_2R_1 = 10^{-6}$ sec.

Example 4.4. A monostable multivibrator is to be used to provide positive pulses with a duration of 41 μsec and a peak amplitude of 12 volts. The trigger source shall be derived from pulses of random width. 2N1306 NPN transistors shall be used. $I_{C(max)} = 300$ ma, $h_{FE(min)} = 60$, and $V_{CC} = 15$ v.

Solution:

(a) Let $I_{C(sat)} = 60$ ma.

(b) $R_L + R_3 = 15/60$ ma $= 250 \, \Omega$

(c) Since the output is to be 12 volts peak, and the output switches from V_E to V_{CC}, then V_E must be 3 volts. Therefore R_3 may be found by a simple ratio.

$$\frac{R_3}{R_L + R_3} = \frac{V_E}{V_{CC}}$$

$$R_3 = 50 \, \Omega$$

(d) R_L is therefore 200 Ω.

(e) R_{B2} is found by Eq. (4-13).

$$R_{B2} = \frac{(V_{CC} - V_E)h_{FE(min)}}{I_{C(sat)}} = \frac{12 \times 60}{60 \times 10^{-3}} = 12 \text{ K}\Omega$$

(f) C_1 is found by use of Eq. (4-1).

$$C_1 = \frac{T}{0.69 \, R_{B2}} = \frac{41 \times 10^{-6}}{0.69 \times 12 \times 10^3}$$
$$= 5 \times 10^{-9} = 0.005 \ \mu\text{fd}$$

(g) Solve for I_B.

$$I_{B1} = \frac{I_{C(sat)}}{h_{FE(min)}} = \frac{60 \times 10^{-3}}{60} = 1 \text{ ma}$$

(h) Solve for R_2 by Eq. (4-14).

$$R_2 = \frac{V_E}{I_2} = \frac{3}{0.1 - 10^{-3}} = 30 \text{ K}\Omega$$

(i) Solve for R_1 by Eq. (4-15).

$$R_1 = \frac{V_{CC} - V_E}{I_{B1} + I_2} = \frac{12}{1.1 \times 10^{-3}} = 10.9 \text{ K}\Omega$$

(j) Solve for C_2.

$$C_2 = \frac{10^{-6}}{R_1} = \frac{10^{-6}}{10.9 \times 10^3} = 92 \text{ pf}$$

(k) It is now appropriate to check the circuit and to make sure that Q_1 will actually be in cutoff during the stable state. In order for Q_1 to be in cutoff, V_{B1} must be less than V_E. This will cause the base of the NPN transistor to be negative with respect to the emitter.

(1) $V_{C2} = V_E + V_{CE(sat)}$ (Assume that $V_{CE(sat)} = 0.2$ v)
    $= 3.2$ v

(2) $V_{B1} = V_{C2}\left(\dfrac{R_2}{R_1 + R_2}\right) = 3.2\left(\dfrac{30 \times 10^3}{41 \times 10^3}\right) = 2.34$ v

(3) We now know that the base of Q_1 is -0.66 volt with respect to the emitter and is, of course, reverse biased.

(l) Now that we have a properly working monostable circuit, we must next consider the shaping of the random pulse inputs into a proper trigger for the monostable multivibrator. Triggering will be covered in detail later in this chapter. For the moment, let us agree that a negative trigger pulse applied to the collector of Q_1 will do the job. A CE inverter circuit can be used to good advantage as the source of negative trigger. Every time an input pulse turns on the inverter, a *negative* trigger equal to the magnitude of V_{CC} is available at the collector of the inverter. Design of the inverter is rudimentary, and the coupling capacitor should be selected so that the time constant determined by $R_{L1}C$ is much smaller than the duration of any of the input pulses.

(m) Capacitor C_3 is not critical, and is only used to maintain V_E at a constant level during the instants of transition from one state to another. So long as the time constant $R_3 C_3$ is at least a few microseconds, the circuit will function properly. In this example, let $C_3 = 0.1$ μfd. This corresponds to a time constant of 5 μsec. Figure 4-21 is a schematic diagram of the completed circuit.

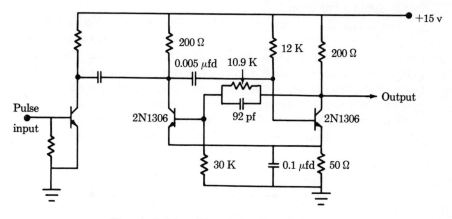

Figure 4-21. Circuit for Example 4.4.

In the example we used a monostable multivibrator to change pulses of random widths into pulses of uniform width and height. Figure 4-22 illustrates the comparison between input pulses and output pulses.

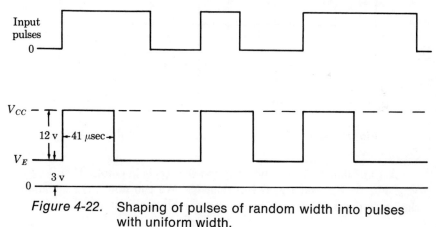

Figure 4-22. Shaping of pulses of random width into pulses with uniform width.

4-4   Bistable Multivibrators

This section shall deal only with saturated types of bistable multivibrators. Non-saturating types will be covered in a following section.

Bistable multivibrators are used in computer applications for shift registers, counters, ring counters, etc. The bistable multivibrator is commonly called a "flip-flop."

The circuit of an emitter-coupled bistable is shown in Figure 4-23.

Unlike the monostable multivibrator, where a stable state was easily discernible from the diagram, the bistable circuit cannot be relied upon to be in a particular state merely by inspection of the circuit diagram. Both states of the bistable are stable ones; therefore, a particular state is dependent upon not only the application of a trigger pulse, but also the immediate past history of the circuit. However, we do know that in each state, one of the transistors is in cutoff while the other is in saturation.

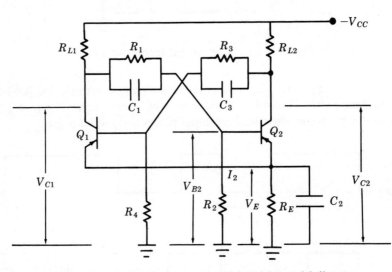

Figure 4-23.   Emitter-coupled bistable multivibrator.

Assume that Q_1 is in saturation and that Q_2 is in cutoff. Then $V_{C2} = V_{CC}$, $V_{C1} = V_E$, and V_{B2} is less than V_E. We can now write equations similar to those for the self-biased monostable multivibrator.

$$V_E = V_{CC}\left(\frac{R_E}{R_E + R_{L1}}\right) \tag{4-16}$$

$$V_{B2} = V_E\left(\frac{R_2}{R_1 + R_2}\right) \tag{4-17}$$

$$V_{B1} = V_E + V_{BE(\text{sat})} \tag{4-18}$$

The speed-up capacitors C_1 and C_3 are both charged. C_1 is charged up to the drop across R_1, and C_3 is charged to approximately $V_{CC} - V_E$.

The capacitor C_2 serves to keep V_E constant during transitions from one state to another.

If a trigger pulse is applied so that Q_1 is driven into cutoff, then the circuit changes to its other stable state where Q_1 remains in cutoff and Q_2 remains in saturation. Under these conditions, V_E remains unchanged, V_{C1} equals V_{CC}, V_{C2} equals V_E, and V_{B1} is less than V_E. Equation (4-18) now applies to V_{B2}, and Equation (4-17) now applies to V_{B1}. If another trigger pulse is applied so that Q_2 is driven into cutoff, the circuit reverts to the conditions described at the beginning of this discussion.

The design of the circuit is based upon some of the equations derived from previous circuits, especially those for the self-biased monostable multivibrator.

1. $I_{C(\text{sat})}$ is made much less than $I_{C(\text{max})}$.

2. Values of R_L and R_E are selected so that with a given V_{CC}, the selected $I_{C(\text{sat})}$ is obtained.

$$R_L + R_E = \frac{V_{CC}}{I_{C(\text{sat})}} \tag{4-12}$$

3. R_E is made much smaller than R_L. Small values of R_E cause outputs to be greater, since the output is equal to $V_{CC} - V_E$. However, just as in the monostable circuit, if V_E is made too small, the circuit will be un-stable at high temperatures. The same practices as in the monostable will apply here. R_E is usually from one-third to one-fourth of R_L.

4. I_B is determined next.

$$I_B = \frac{I_{C(\text{sat})}}{h_{FE(\text{min})}}$$

Since $I_{C(\text{sat})} = \dfrac{V_{CC}}{R_E + R_L}$

then, $\quad I_B = \dfrac{V_{CC}}{(R_E + R_L)h_{FE(\text{min})}} \tag{4-19}$

5. The current through R_2 or R_4 is chosen to be a small fraction of I_B. We shall assume that these currents are one-tenth of I_B.

6. The resistors R_2 and R_4 are found.

$$R_2 = R_4 = \frac{V_E}{I_2} \tag{4-14}$$

7. The resistors R_1 and R_3 are found.

$$R_1 = R_3 = \frac{V_{CC} - V_E}{I_B + I_2} \tag{4-15}$$

8. The speed-up capacitors are chosen so that the time constants of the circuits is one microsecond.

Example 4.5.   Design an emitter-coupled bistable multivibrator with an output voltage swing of -9 volts peak. Type 2N394 PNP transistors shall be used. $I_{C(max)} = 200$ ma, $h_{FE(min)} = 20$, and $V_{CC} = -15$ v.

Solution:

   (a) Select $I_{C(sat)}$. In this example, let $I_{C(sat)} = 10$ ma.

   (b) Solve for $R_E + R_L$. [Eq. (4-12)]

$$R_E + R_L = \frac{V_{CC}}{I_{C(sat)}} = \frac{15}{10 \times 10^{-3}} = 1500 \ \Omega$$

   (c) The output voltage swing is 9 v; therefore, $V_E = -6$ v. R_E is found from the proportion

$$\frac{R_E}{R_E + R_L} = \frac{V_E}{V_{CC}}$$

$$R_E = \frac{1500 \times 6}{15} = 600 \ \Omega$$

   (d) R_L is found by subtracting R_E from $(R_E + R_L)$.

$$R_L = 900 \ \Omega$$

   (e) I_B is found by use of Eq. (4-19).

$$I_B = \frac{V_{CC}}{(R_E + R_L)h_{FE(min)}}$$

$$= \frac{15}{1.5 \times 10^3 \times 20} = 0.5 \text{ ma}$$

   (f) I_2 is chosen as $0.1 \ I_B$.

$$I_2 = 50 \ \mu a$$

   (g) R_2 and R_4 are found. [Eq. (4-14)].

$$R_2 = R_4 = V_E/I_2 = 6/50 \times 10^{-6} = 120 \text{ K}\Omega$$

   (h) R_1 and R_3 are found by Eq. (4-15).

$$R_1 = R_3 = \frac{V_{CC} - V_E}{I_B + I_2} = \frac{9}{0.55 \times 10^{-3}} = 16.4 \text{ K}\Omega$$

   (i) C_1 and C_3 are found.

$$C_1 = C_3 = \frac{10^{-6}}{16.4 \times 10^3} = 61 \text{ pf}$$

   (j) It would now be wise to determine if R_1 and R_2 (also R_3 and R_4) have been selected so that a transistor can be cut off. If we assume that Q_1 is in saturation, then Q_2 must be in cutoff.

$$V_{B2} = -6 \times \frac{120 \times 10^3}{136 \times 10^3} = -5.3 \text{ v}$$

This means that the base of Q_2 is 0.7 positive with respect to the emitter. This is more than enough to cause Q_2 to be in cutoff.

If at any time more reverse bias is desired, it is only necessary to make I_2 larger, which then reduces R_2.

Figure 4-24 shows the completed circuit.

(k) A 0.02 μfd capacitor is used to bypass R_E giving a time constant of 12 μsec, more than enough time to hold V_E constant during transitions.

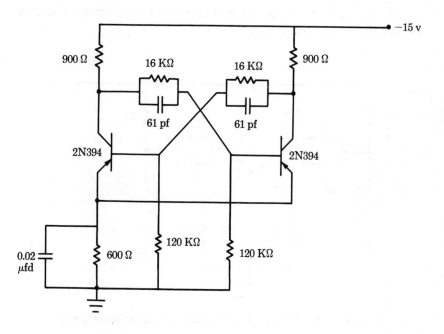

Figure 4-24.   Circuit for Example 4.5.

A common circuit arrangement of the bistable multivibrator is illustrated in Figure 4-25. In this circuit the reverse-bias voltage for the OFF unit is obtained from an external source rather than from the drop across an emitter resistor. The circuit will provide a larger voltage output for a given collector source than the emitter-coupled type.

Operation of this circuit requires that one transistor be in cutoff, while the other is in saturation. The cross-coupling networks $R_1 - R_2$ and $R_3 - R_4$ are chosen so that there is sufficient forward bias available to the ON unit. There is never any problem in supplying sufficient reverse

bias to maintain a unit OFF, provided that the other transistor is in saturation. If we assume that Q_1 is in cutoff, then Q_2 is in saturation. To
maintain Q_1 in cutoff, it is only necessary that V_{BB} be greater than
$V_{CE(sat)}$. The voltages around the circuit are then:

$$V_{CE1} \approx V_{CC} \quad (R_1 \gg R_{L1})$$
$$V_{BE1} = V_{BB}$$
$$V_{CE2} \approx 0$$
$$V_{BE2} \approx 300 \text{ mv}$$

The design of the circuit is based upon the same techniques used in
the astable and monostable multivibrators.

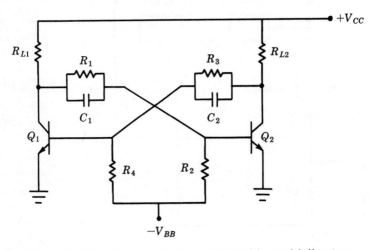

Figure 4-25.   Externally biased bistable multivibrator.

1. Select some value of $I_{C(sat)} < I_{C(max)}$.

2. Calculate R_L. Let $R_{L1} = R_{L2}$.

$$R_L = \frac{V_{CC}}{I_{C(sat)}}$$

3. Calculate I_B.

$$I_B = \frac{I_{C(sat)}}{h_{FE(min)}}$$

4. Calculate R_2. The equivalent circuit for this calculation is shown in
   Figure 4-26.

    a. Let I_2 be much less than I_{B2}.

b. Solve for R_2.

$$R_2 = \frac{|V_{BB}| + |V_{BE}|}{I_2} \qquad (4\text{-}7)$$

5. Solve for R_1. The equivalent circuit of Figure 4-26 is used to obtain the equation for R_2.

$$R_1 = \frac{|V_{CC}| - |V_{BE}|}{I_B + I_2} - R_L \qquad (4\text{-}8)$$

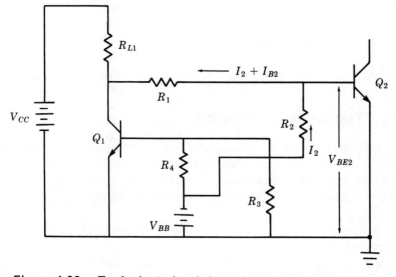

Figure 4-26. Equivalent circuit for calculation of R_2 in Figure 4-25.

Example 4.6. Type 2N1301 PNP transistors are to be used in the bistable circuit of Figure 4-25. $V_{CE(max)} = -12$ v, $I_{C(max)} = 100$ ma, and $h_{FE(min)} = 50$. Let $V_{CC} = -9$ v and $V_{BB} = +1.5$ v.

Solution:

(a) Let $I_{C(sat)} = 19$ ma.

(b) $R_{L1} = R_{L2}$

$$R_L = \frac{V_{CC}}{I_{C(sat)}} = \frac{9}{19 \times 10^{-3}} = 470 \ \Omega$$

(c) Calculate I_B.

$$I_B = \frac{I_{C(sat)}}{h_{FE(min)}} = \frac{19 \times 10^{-3}}{50} = 0.38 \text{ ma}$$

(d) Calculate R_2.

(1) Assume that $I_2 = 0.038$ ma.

(2) Let $R_2 = R_4$.

$$R_2 = \frac{|V_{BB}| + |V_{BE}|}{I_2} = \frac{1.5 + 0.3}{0.38 \times 10^{-4}} = 47 \text{ K}\Omega$$

(e) Calculate R_1 and R_3. Let $R_1 = R_3$.

$$R_1 = \frac{|V_{CC}| - |V_{BE}|}{I_B + I_2} - R_{L1}$$

$$= \frac{9 - 0.3}{0.418 \times 10^{-3}} - 470 \cong 20 \text{ K}\Omega$$

(f) Calculate C_1 and C_2.

$$C_1 = C_2 = \frac{10^{-6}}{R_1} = \frac{10^{-6}}{20 \times 10^3} = 50 \text{ pf}$$

4-5 Triggering Techniques

Up to this point in our discussion of regenerative switching circuits, we have discussed triggering in connection with monostable and bistable multivibrators, but no explanations about triggering have been given. This section will deal with the proper techniques for supplying triggers to these circuits.

A transition from one state to another can be accomplished in mono-stable and bistable multivibrators in either of two ways:

(1) A trigger can be applied to an ON unit so that the ON unit shuts OFF, which in turn causes the OFF unit to come ON.

(2) A trigger pulse can be applied to an OFF unit, turning it ON, which in turn causes the ON unit to be switched OFF.

Either method is practical; however, the method described in (1) affords a more efficient use of the trigger pulse. The ON transistor is an amplifier. A trigger pulse need only be larger than V_{BE} to cause the transistor to cut off. When the transistor cuts off, the collector voltage of the transistor rises and switches the other transistor out of cutoff. It we apply our trigger pulse to the OFF unit, then the trigger must be larger than whatever back bias we may have upon the base of the transistor. In addition, some transistors have slow turn-on characteristics, which could cause some delay in switching unless the turn-on pulse is of large amplitude. When a trigger is used to turn OFF a transistor, the regenerative switching causes the other side to turn ON.

In the case of monostable multivibrator there are two desirable trigger points. One is at the collector of the transistor that is OFF in the stable

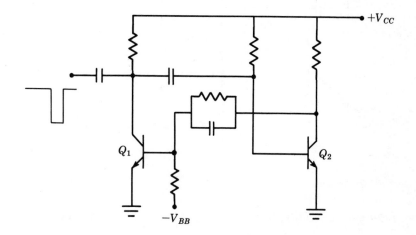

Figure 4-27.   Trigger applied to the collector of the OFF transistor.

state; the other is at the base of the transistor that is ON when in the stable
state. Figures 4-27 and 4-28 show both circuits. The reader will note that
in either circuit arrangement, the pulse is applied to the base of the ON
unit as a turn-off pulse. The circuit of Figure 4-27 offers less loading on
a pulse source than Figure 4-28. In both cases capacitors are used to
couple the trigger pulses. In monostable circuits, the maximum triggering
rate is limited by the duration of the quasi-stable state of the circuit. The
time between trigger pulses must always be greater than the duration (recovery time) of the quasi-stable state.

The reader will recall that a bistable multivibrator has two stable states.
In applying trigger to a bistable, the trigger may be used to set the bistable
into a particular state, such as in resetting a counter, or the trigger may
simply be used to switch the bistable from one state to another. When a
trigger pulse is applied to a bistable circuit in such a manner that only one
particular side of the bistable can be affected by the trigger pulse, this

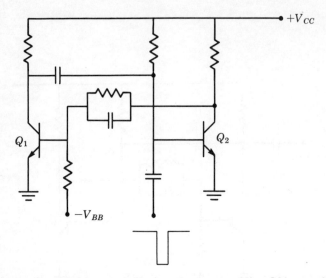

Figure 4-28.   Trigger applied to the base of the ON transistor.

method of trigger is called *asymmetrical triggering*. When asymmetrical triggering is used, the trigger pulse can only be effective if the bistable circuit is in a particular state. For example, if we assume that Q_1 is in saturation and that Q_2 is in cutoff, and we apply an OFF trigger to the base of Q_2, *no transition will take place*. On the other hand, if Q_2 is in saturation at the time that the trigger is applied to the base of Q_2, then the circuit will switch, and Q_2 will go into cutoff, driving Q_1 into saturation.

When *symmetrical triggering* is used in a bistable circuit, *every* trigger pulse causes the circuit to switch states. The pulse is applied through *steering circuits* so that each application of a trigger pulse is guided to the proper side of the bistable circuit. This type of triggering is used in counters and in shift registers. In the arithmetic circuits of digital computers, bistable multivibrators are used for many applications. In some cases a single bistable multivibrator will have both symmetrical and asymmetrical trigger inputs. Obviously this must be true of a counter circuit. The symmetrical trigger is used to advance the count, while the asymmetrical trigger is used for reset purposes.

(a) Symmetrical Collector Triggering.   The circuit of Figure 4-29 shows an emitter-coupled bistable circuit with symmetrical trigger applied to the collectors. The diodes D_1 and D_2 form the steering circuit in conjunction with the resistor R_A. If we assume that Q_1 is in cutoff and Q_2 is in saturation, then the voltage across D_1 is such that it is forward biased, while the voltage across D_2 is a reverse bias. When a positive trigger pulse appears at the junction of D_1 and D_2, the pulse will be guided by D_1 to the collector of Q_1. The reverse bias on D_2 prevents the pulse from appearing at the collector of Q_2. The voltage at the collector of Q_1 rises. This rise is immediately coupled through C_1 to the base of Q_2. Then Q_2 is driven into cutoff, and the circuit switches from one stable state to the other. After the transition, Q_1 is in cutoff and Q_2 is in saturation. Now D_1 is reverse biased and D_2 is forward biased. When a trigger pulse is applied, it is "steered" through D_2 to the collector of Q_2. This again is a turn-off pulse to the base of Q_1, and another transition takes place.

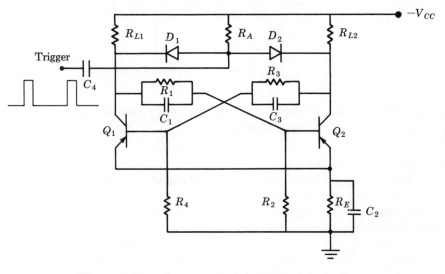

Figure 4-29.   Symmetrical collector triggering.

The bias resistor R_A should be large to minimize loading on the trigger source. However, R_A should be as small as possible to permit rapid recharging of the input capacitor C_4. Then C_4 and R_A form a differentiating network, changing the input pulses into differentiated spikes of short duration. Where the peak-to-peak voltage swing of the pulse source is greater than $|V_{CC}|$, the bias resistor R_A can be replaced by a diode. The use of a diode in place of R_A improves the performance of the triggering circuit, permitting a greater trigger rate. During the period of time when an input trigger can be effective (positive swing in Figure 4-29) the diode is back biased, and this high impedance offers minimum loading upon the pulse source. When the input pulse swings negative, the diode becomes forward

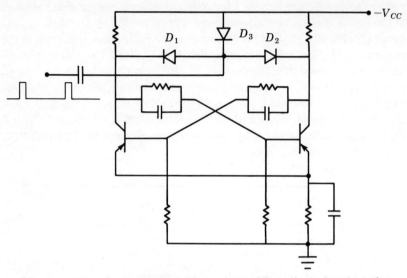

Figure 4-30. Symmetrical triggering with a diode load on the trigger source.

biased and permits rapid recovery of charge on the input capacitor. The circuit of Figure 4-30 illustrates the use of a diode in place of R_A.

Collector triggering offers the advantages of minimum loading upon the pulse source and high speed of transition. The application of the pulse to the proper collector aids in speeding the change of states since the direction of the applied pulse is the same as that of the collector voltage change during the transition. Trigger pulse amplitude is not critical in collector triggering, and large variations in trigger amplitude are possible.

(b) Symmetrical Base Triggering. The circuit of Figure 4-31 shows a bistable multivibrator with symmetrical trigger applied to the bases. A lesser amount of trigger energy is required than in collector triggering, but the pulse amplitude must be more carefully controlled. The quantitative difference between base voltages is less than the difference between collector voltages, hence the need for more accurate control of trigger amplitude. If too large a trigger is applied, the steering circuit will not operate properly. If we assume that Q_1 of Figure 4-31 is in saturation and that Q_2 is in cutoff, then V_{BE1} is slightly positive and V_{BE2} is some voltage negative with respect to ground. Therefore, diode D_1 is in a forward-biased condition while D_2 is reverse biased. When the input trigger swings negative, D_1 will direct the pulse to the base of Q_1 while D_2 will offer a high impedance path

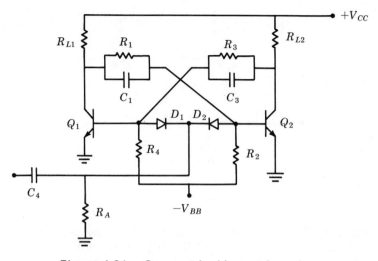

Figure 4-31. Symmetrical base triggering.

to the base of Q_2. The negative trigger is a turn-off to the base of Q_1 and the circuit switches. To increase triggering rate, R_A can be replaced with a diode as in Figure 4-32.

(c) Base Triggering With a Hybrid Steering. A hybrid steering arrangement as in Figure 4-33 combines the advantages of base and collector steering techniques. The circuit has the sensitivity of base triggering (low trigger power needed) and trigger amplitude tolerance of collector triggering. In the circuit shown, diodes D_1 and D_2 are used for steering. The voltages across the diodes are the collector-to-base voltages of the transistors. The V_{CB} of the transistor in saturation is small, while V_{CB} of the cutoff transistor is high. Therefore, if we assume that Q_1 is in cutoff and Q_2 is in saturation, then D_1 is reverse biased and D_2 has a negligible voltage across it. When a trigger pulse is applied, the pulse is then directed to the base of Q_2, causing a transition from one stable state to the other.

Up to this point in our discussion of bistable multivibrators, all explanations have used saturated switching. Non-saturating techniques can be used with any of the circuits we have so far discussed. Figure 4-34 shows a non-saturated bistable multivibrator with hybrid steering for a symmetrical trigger plus asymmetrical trigger input terminals. In computer terminology, we can refer to the symmetrical input terminal as the *complement* input, and the asymmetrical input terminals as *set* and *reset* inputs.

Symmetrical collector triggering can also be accomplished by use of a

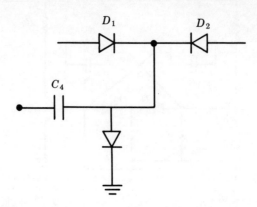

Figure 4-32. Triggering rate is increased by the use of a diode load on the trigger source.

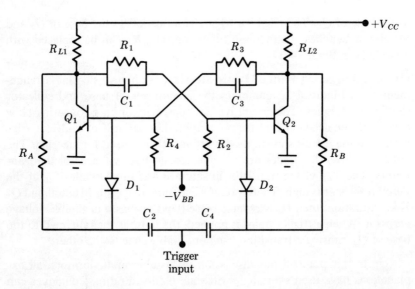

Figure 4-33. Symmetrical base triggering with hybrid steering.

trigger amplifier. This permits the use of small trigger amplitudes while retaining all of the advantages of collector triggering. The use of a transistor eliminates the need for the diode D_3 of Figure 4-30. A circuit using a trigger amplifier is shown in Figure 4-35. Collector voltage for Q_3 is supplied

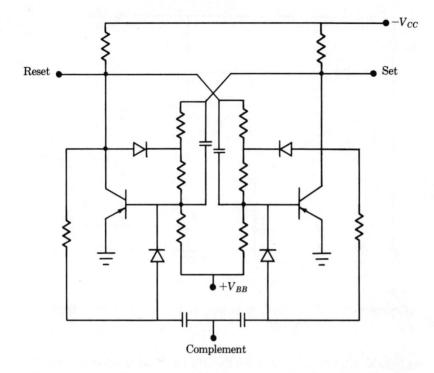

Figure 4-34. High speed bistable multivibrator with hybrid
base triggering.

through the diode that is connected to the collector of the OFF transistor
of the bistable circuit. When a positive input is applied to the base of Q_3
the transistor conducts. The collector current of Q_3 must then flow through
the load resistance of the OFF transistor of the bistable causing V_{ce} for that
transistor to drop, supplying an OFF pulse to the base of the ON transistor.
For example, if we assume that Q_1 is in saturation and that Q_2 is in cutoff,
then collector supply for Q_3 is obtained through D_2. When a positive pulse
appears at the base of Q_3, the collector current of Q_3 flows through R_{L2}
causing the voltage at the junction of R_{L2} and the collector of Q_2 to drop.
Because the cross-coupling capacitor C_3 cannot change charge instantaneously, a negative pulse is coupled to the base of Q_1, driving Q_1 into cutoff.
The use of a trigger amplifier is particularly attractive for applications in
which high speed and reliable switching are needed.

   Another symmetrical triggering technique that may be used makes use
of the cross-coupling capacitors as *commutating capacitors*. This method
of triggering is useful in counter circuits where the change in V_{CE} of a
transistor as the count is advanced can be used as a trigger for the follow-

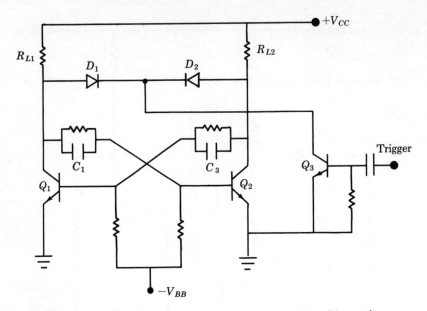

Figure 4-35.   Symmetrical collector triggering with a trigger amplifier.

ing bistable circuit. In Figure 4-36 the collector load resistors are returned to the collector source through a common resistor R_T. If a negative pulse is applied at the junction of R_T and the load resistors, the bistable multivibrator will change states. To explain how steering is accomplished without the use of diodes, we shall assume some operating potentials for the circuit of Figure 4-36. These voltages are shown on the circuit.

Assume that a negative pulse of 10 volts is applied to the trigger terminal. Both transistors are driven into cutoff, and the voltage at both collectors is now 5 volts. The cross-coupling capacitors cannot change charge instantly. Therefore the base voltages must change in order to satisfy the requirement that any voltage loop must add up to zero volts. The base of Q_1 must go positive while Q_2 must go negative. It is apparent from the circuit potentials shown in Figure 4-36 that we assumed that Q_1 was in cutoff and Q_2 in saturation. The change in base voltages when the trigger pulse is applied causes a change of states, turning Q_1 ON and driving Q_2 OFF. A more detailed analysis can be seen by referring to Figure 4-37(a) and (b). Prior to the application of the trigger pulse, C_1 was charged to 10 volts and C_3 was charged to 2 volts. When both collector voltages drop to 5 volts, the base of Q_2 must go 5 volts negative in order for the algebraic sum of the voltages around the loop shown in Figure 4-37(a) to be zero.

On the other hand, the base of Q_1 must be 3 volts positive in order for voltage loop in the circuit of Figure 4-37(b) to be zero.

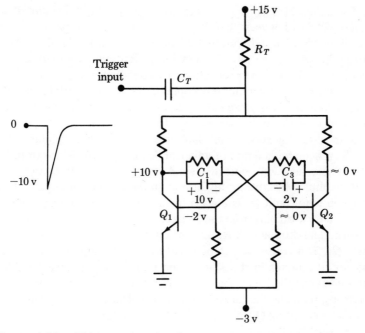

Figure 4-36. Trigger steering by use of commutating capacitors.

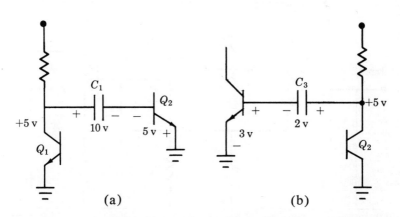

Figure 4-37. Voltage distribution at the bases Q_1 and Q_2 after a trigger pulse has been applied.

4-6 The Schmitt Trigger

The Schmitt trigger is a regeneratively coupled bistable circuit whose output switches between two fixed voltage levels. The particular output level of the circuit is a discontinuous function of the amplitude of the input voltage. The circuit is useful for signal level shifting, the squaring of sinusoidal inputs, and for the restoration of pulses that have become deteriorated. In the digital computer it becomes necessary to discriminate between pulses and noise. Noise can cause erratic switching as well as a degenerative change in the pulse waveform. The Schmitt trigger is particularly useful in reshaping such signals into clearly defined rectangular pulses.

The schematic diagram of a typical Schmitt trigger is shown in Figure 4-38. The reader will note the similarity between this circuit and the emitter-coupled bistable multivibrator. In the absence of any inputs, Q_1 is always in cutoff and Q_2 is always in saturation. This is true because Q_2 receives a forward bias from the collector of Q_1 through the cross-coupling network. The drop across R_E as a result of the conduction of Q_2 reverse biases Q_1. This causes V_{C1} to be equal to V_{CC}, driving Q_2 into saturation. The circuit remains in this stable state until an input signal of sufficient amplitude is applied such that Q_1 becomes forward biased. At this point, V_{C1} drops, reducing the forward bias on Q_2. This causes the voltage V_E to decrease, permitting Q_1 to saturate. When Q_1 saturates, $V_{C1} = V_E$ and Q_2

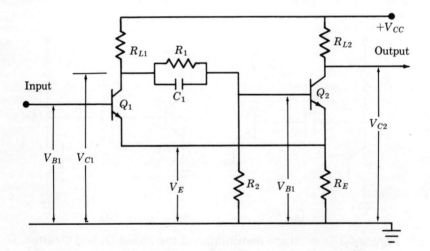

Figure 4-38. Schmitt trigger.

is now in cutoff. The output voltage will now remain at V_{CC} until the signal level drops to a value low enough to cause Q_1 to move out of saturation. At this instant V_{C1} starts to rise, V_E decreases, and Q_2 again conducts. The emitter current of Q_2 causes the drop across R_E to rise again, further reducing the collector current of Q_1 and further raising V_{C1}. The increase in V_{C1} drives Q_2 into saturation, cutting off Q_1. Thus the output voltage at the collector of Q_2 is a rectangular wave. The reader will note that the inputs needed to change output levels were not the same. The input level at which Q_1 turns ON is called the *upper trigger point* (UTP), and the input level at which Q_2 turns ON is called the *lower trigger point* (LTP). This "backlash" or hysteresis is characteristic of all Schmitt trigger circuits.

Figure 4-39 illustrates the Schmitt trigger using PNP transistors. Let us use this circuit to make a quantitative analysis of the operation of the Schmitt trigger. If we assume that the input voltage is zero, then surely Q_1 is in cutoff and Q_2 is in saturation. Circuit potentials are readily found:

$$V_E = V_{CC}\left(\frac{R_E}{R_E + R_L}\right) = -12 \times \frac{560}{2,360} = -2.85 \text{ v}$$

$$V_{CE2} \approx 0$$
$$V_{C2} \approx -2.85 \text{ v}$$
$$V_{BE2} \approx -250 \text{ mv}$$
$$V_{B2} \approx -3.1 \text{ v}$$
$$V_{BE1} = +2.85 \text{ v.}$$

(Assuming that $V_{B1} = 0$. In any event V_{BE1} is always equal to the difference between V_{B1} and V_E.)

$$V_{CE1} = V_{CC} - V_E = -9.15 \text{ v}$$
$$V_{C1} \approx V_{CC} \approx -12 \text{ v}$$

For the operating conditions described, the output voltage level is approximately -2.85 volts.

When the input voltage becomes slightly more negative than V_E, then Q_1 is turned ON and Q_2 is driven into cutoff. Operating potentials for this condition are now found:

$$V_E = -2.85 \text{ v.}$$

(This is so because the load resistors for the two transistors are the same.)

$$V_{CE2} = V_{CC} - V_E = -9.15 \text{ v}$$
$$V_{C2} = -12 \text{ v}$$
$$V_{B2} = V_{C1}\left(\frac{R_2}{R_1 + R_2}\right) = -2.85 \times \frac{15 \times 10^3}{33 \times 10^3} = -1.3 \text{ v}$$
$$V_{BE2} = V_{B2} - V_E = -1.3 - (-2.85) = +1.55 \text{ v}$$
$$V_{BE1} \cong -250 \text{ mv}$$
$$V_{CE1} \approx 0$$

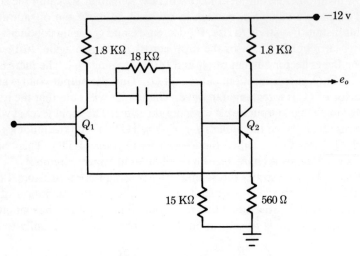

Figure 4-39.   PNP Schmitt trigger.

The output level for the conditions described is -12 volts.

In order for the circuit to revert back to an output level of -2.85 volts, Q_1 must go into cutoff. As the signal voltage rises towards zero, Q_1 is *not* cut off when the signal becomes equal to -2.85 volts. This is simply due to the fact that the transistor cannot cut itself off by means of its own emitter current. Current flow in Q_1 simply decreases, reducing V_E and maintaining Q_1 in saturation. However, as the current decreases, V_{C1} increases. Finally a point is reached where Q_2 begins to conduct. This starts a regenerative process. The current flow of Q_2 increases V_E, which in turn increases V_{C1}, which further increases the current flow in Q_2. This process continues until Q_2 is in saturation and Q_1 is in cutoff. The description of the process may make it sound as if the switch of Q_2 from cutoff to saturation is a slow procedure. In actuality the switching process is almost instantaneous and results in an abrupt change of output level. Figure 4-40 illustrates the appearance of the input and output voltages for the circuit of Figure 4-39. Note that in this sketch the UTP appears below the LTP. These trigger points are shown in this manner in order to be consistent with our definition of LTP and UTP. In addition the UTP is a greater amount of voltage than the LTP, just as should be expected in a Schmitt trigger circuit.

We can now see the backlash in a Schmitt trigger more clearly. At time t_1 the lower trigger point is reached, Q_1 goes into cutoff and Q_2 into saturation. The circuit remains in this state even though at time t_2 the input

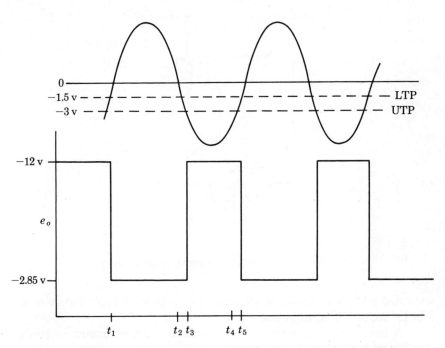

Figure 4-40.   Input and output waveforms of a Schmitt trigger.

signal is again at the LTP. The circuit changes states at time t_3 when the upper trigger point is reached. The time interval $(t_3 - t_2)$ is the backlash. The upper and lower trigger points can be changed by changing R_1 and R_2 and/or R_E. It is a common practice to make R_E a variable resistor so that the UTP and LTP may be modified as the circuit components age.

4-7 Blocking Oscillators

Up to this point in the chapter, all of the regenerative switching circuits discussed have made use of two transistors. In the blocking oscillator circuit, a transformer (usually a pulse transformer) will be used to provide positive feedback from the output to the input circuits. Blocking oscillators may be either astable or monostable. The astable circuit is frequently used as a source of pulses and, also, in the generation of sawtooth waves. The monostable circuit is widely used in pulse circuitry because of its ability to develop an output pulse of short duration with nearly vertical

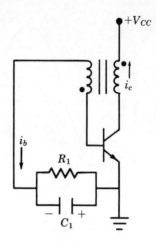

Figure 4-41.   Common emitter oscillator.

rise and fall times. Hence, in pulse circuitry its primary application would be for the reshaping of pulses.

A basic astable common emitter blocking oscillator circuit is shown in Figure 4-41. Note that the transformer is connected into the circuit so that 180° phase shift occurs between the collector and the base. When first turned on, the only current flow in the collector circuit is leakage current. This current then causes a voltage to be induced in the base circuit winding that forward biases the base-to-emitter junction. This increases collector current, which in turn increases the forward bias on the base. This will cause more collector current flow, which in turn causes more forward bias until the collector circuit is driven into saturation. When the circuit saturates, there is no further change in the magnetic field established by the collector winding; therefore, there is no voltage developed across the base winding of the transformer. The transistor is no longer forward biased, and collector current drops. The drop in collector current causes a back emf to be developed in the collector winding, and also a voltage is induced into the base winding that drives the transistor deep into cutoff. During the short interval that the transistor was conducting, base current flow charged the capacitor C_1. When base current flow stops, the capacitor discharges to the point where collector current can flow again. The transistor remains in cutoff. The cycle of operation then repeats itself. Waveforms of collector and base voltages are shown in Figure 4-42. The reader will note that the voltage at the collector at the instant the transistor

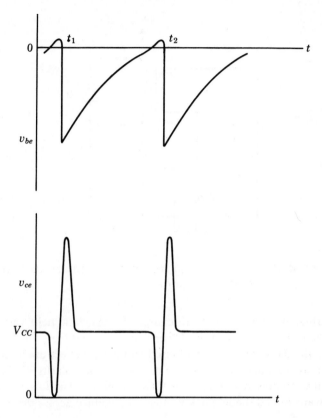

Figure 4-42. Base and collector voltage waveform for a blocking oscillator.

is driven into cutoff is much greater than collector supply voltage. This is, of course, due to the fact that the transformer winding is acting as a voltage source in attempting to maintain current flow, and the actual v_{ce} at this instant is the sum of V_{CC} and the induced emf across the transformer winding. In most cases this voltage will be great enough to cause an avalanche breakdown between collector and base. An additional fault with the basic circuit is that the collector is permitted to go into saturation. This will cause storage time delay and limit the minimum pulse width that may be obtained. Both the problems of saturation and avalanche breakdown can be avoided by the use of diodes as shown in Figure 4-43.

Diode D_1 of Figure 4-43 is connected as a simple voltage clamp to keep the transistor out of saturation. Diode D_2 is connected across the

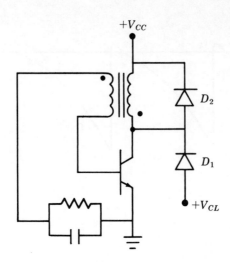

Figure 4-43. CE blocking oscillator with protective and clamping diode.

transformer winding so as to discharge the magnetic field very quickly when the transistor is in cutoff. During the time that the transistor is conducting, the diode D_2 is reverse biased and has no effect upon the circuit. As soon as the transistor goes into cutoff and the polarity of the voltage across the winding reverses, D_2 is forward biased. The low resistance of the forward-biased diode quickly causes the voltage across the winding to be zero.

In many applications, the transformer has a tertiary winding from which the actual output voltages are taken. This gives the circuit designer greater freedom of design, as diodes can be connected to this winding to limit both positive and negative excursions of the output voltage. Figure 4-44 is an example of a common emitter astable circuit with a tertiary winding for the output voltage.

The common base circuit may also be used for an astable blocking oscillator. This circuit requires the use of two voltage supplies, and is shown in Figure 4-45. The operation of the circuit is readily explained. The emitter junction is forward biased by V_{EE}. Collector current flow induces a voltage into the secondary winding that further increases the forward bias on the emitter. When the transformer core saturates, no further flux changes occur and, thus, the forward bias developed across the secondary is removed. The capacitor C_1 which was charged during the period of conduction for the transistor is now directly across the emitter-

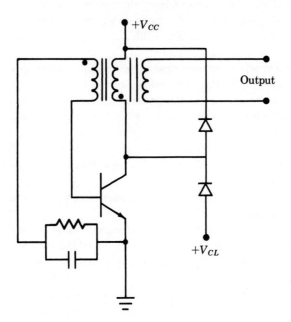

Figure 4-44. CE blocking oscillator with separate output winding.

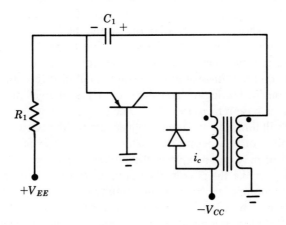

Figure 4-45. Common base blocking oscillator.

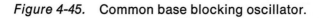

to-base junction. This reverse biases the junction, driving the transistor into cutoff. The transistor will remain in cutoff until the charge on the capacitor approximates zero. When this happens, the bias source V_{EE} will forward bias the transistor, causing another cycle of operation to start. Once again a diode is needed across the collector winding of the transformer to prevent avalanche breakdown of the collector junction as a result of the induced emf across the primary winding at the instant of cutoff.

Monostable blocking oscillators can be either common base or common emitter forms. In both cases a reverse-bias source must be used to keep the transistor in cutoff until a trigger pulse is applied. When trigger is applied, the transistor conducts. The regenerative feedback increases the forward bias on the transistor until either the transistor clamps or the transformer core saturates. The unit then drops back into cutoff until the next trigger pulse is applied.

A common emitter monostable blocking oscillator is shown in Figure 4-46. In the stable state the base-to-emitter voltage is $-V_{BB}$. When an input trigger is applied, collector current flow causes v_{ce} to drop. As in the astable circuit, the transformer is connected so as to induce a base voltage of opposite polarity from the collector voltage. The base is driven positive, increasing collector current until D_1 conducts, thus clamping the collector voltage to V_{CL}. The magnetizing current of collector winding now becomes constant, and no further coupling to the base circuit occurs. Collector current begins to fall, and the field around the collector winding begins to collapse, inducing a voltage of opposite polarity across the collector winding. This reverse pulse of voltage is induced into the base winding, driving it deep into cutoff. The diode D_2 quickly discharges the collector winding field and also prevents avalanche breakdown of the transistor.

During the short active period of the circuit, the forward bias developed across the base winding of the transformer has to be greater than $|V_{BB}|$. The base current flow developed a charge across C_1 as shown. The actual reverse bias on the transistor at the instant of cutoff is the sum of V_{BB} and the charge on C_1. During the stable period, C_1 discharges through R_1 and the bias on the base returns to $-V_{BB}$. The time constant R_1C_1 is the major factor that will limit the maximum trigger rate for the circuit.

Low values of V_{BB} permit the use of smaller trigger pulse amplitudes, but the circuit may be unstable in the presence of noise. Although larger values of V_{BB} make the circuit more immune to noise and other interferences, they require much more pulse amplitude.

The common base version of a monostable blocking oscillator is shown in Figure 4-47. When a positive trigger pulse is applied, collector current flow through the primary winding induces a forward-bias voltage on the

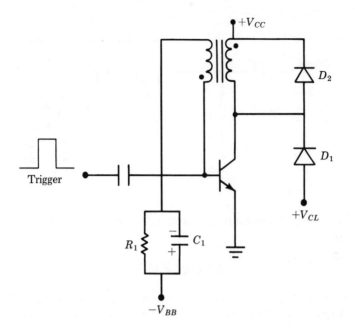

Figure 4-46.   Common emitter monostable blocking oscilla-
              tor.

emitter winding. This causes an increase in collector current, with a corresponding increase in emitter current until the transformer core saturates.
No feedback to the emitter is then obtained, and collector current starts
to drop, causing an induced emf of opposite polarity to be developed
across the primary. As a result of the decreasing magnetic field, the emitter
is driven negative, thus cutting off the transistor. The capacitor C_1 discharges through R_1 and the secondary of the transformer. In this circuit
the discharge of C_1 is aided by the voltage across the secondary at the
instant the transistor goes into cutoff. Maximum trigger rate is limited by
the R_1C_1 time constant and the secondary inductance of the transformer.

     The reader will note that in the common base circuits the feedback
loop is in shunt with the reverse-bias source; hence, the feedback requirements are not so rigorous as those for the common emitter circuit. Again,
large values of V_{EE} make the circuit more stable at the expense of larger
trigger amplitude requirements.

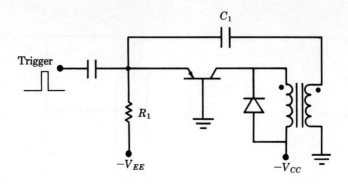

Figure 4-47.   Common base monostable blocking oscillator.

PROBLEMS

4.1.   Draw a schematic diagram of an astable multivibrator using PNP transistors. Indicate the charge and discharge paths of the capacitors.

4.2.   A certain NPN transistor has the following parameters: $h_{FE(min)} = 20$, $I_{C(max)} = 150$ ma, and $V_{CE(max)} = 45$ v. Let the collector supply $= +25$ v and $I_{C(sat)} = 92.5$ ma. Design an astable multivibrator to produce the waveform shown in Figure 4-48.

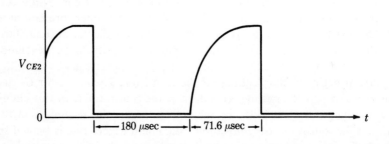

Figure 4-48.   Output waveform for Problem 4.2.

4.3.   A certain astable multivibrator develops the output waveform shown in Figure 4-49. (a) What is the collector supply voltage? (b) What is the product $R_{B1}C_2$? (c) What is the product $R_{B2}C_1$?

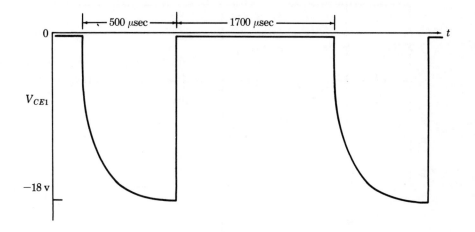

Figure 4-49. Output waveform for Problem 4.3.

4.4. Use the transistor circuit constants of Problem 4-2 and design a symmetrical multivibrator for a frequency of 8 kc/s. Let $V_{CC} = 20$ volts, and $I_{C(sat)} = 26.7$ ma.

4.5. The circuit of Figure 4-50 is to be used to obtain the waveform shown. PNP transistors are to be used. Let $h_{FE(min)} = 40$, $I_{C(max)} = 75$ ma, $V_{CE(max)} = -18$ v, and $I_{C(sat)} = 41$ ma. Calculate the components of the circuit.

4.6. A switching system requires the pulse inputs shown in Figure 4-51. Draw a block diagram showing how astable and monostable multivibrators can be used to obtain the required pulses.

4.7. Design a monostable multivibrator to develop rectangular pulses of approximately 60 μsec duration. Use the transistor parameters of Problem 4-5. Use a base-bias supply of $+1.5$ v and a collector supply of -6 volts. Let $I_{C(sat)} = 12.8$ ma, and assume that $V_{BE(sat)} = 300$ mv.

4.8. The transistors of Problem 4-2 are to be used in a monostable multivibrator circuit. The circuit is to produce a negative pulse approximately 5 μsec after a trigger pulse is applied. Let $I_{C(sat)} = 60$ ma, $V_{CC} = +20$ v, $V_{BB} = -0.5$ v, and $V_{BE(sat)} = 250$ mv. Calculate all of the circuit components.

4.9. A self-biased monostable multivibrator is to be used to provide positive pulses with an approximate duration of 18 μsec and a peak amplitude of 15 v. NPN transistors will be used. Let $h_{FE(min)} = 50$, $I_{C(max)} = 200$ ma, $V_{CC} = 20$ v, and $I_{C(sat)} = 80$ ma. Design the circuit.

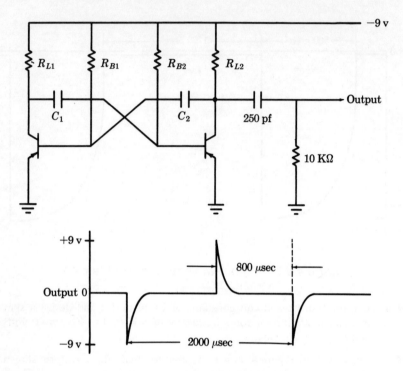

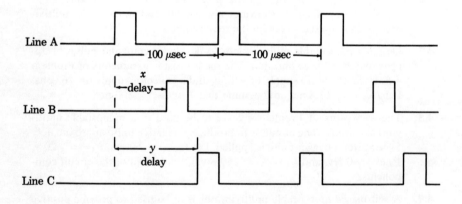

Figure 4-50.   Circuit for Problem 4.5.

Figure 4-51.   Pulse outputs for Problem 4.6.

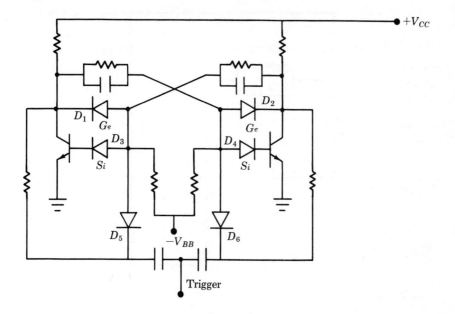

Figure 4-52.   Circuit for Problem 4.14.

4.10. Redesign the circuit of Problem 4-9 into an emitter-coupled bistable circuit.

4.11. Design a bistable multivibrator as in Figure 4-25. Use PNP transistors. Let $h_{FE(min)} = 35$, $I_{C(max)} = 80$, $V_{CC} = -18$ v, $V_{BB} = +3$ v, and $I_{C(sat)} = 20$ ma. Assume that $V_{BE(sat)} = 700$ mv.

4.12. Draw the diagram of the circuit of Problem 4-11. Using diode steering, show how collector triggering can be applied to the circuit.

4.13. Explain why collector triggering requires a greater trigger amplitude than base triggering of a bistable multivibrator.

4.14. Explain the functions of the diodes in the circuit of Figure 4-52.

4.15. Approximate the upper and lower trigger points for the circuit of Figure 4-53.

4.16. Draw a schematic diagram of a scale of 8 binary counter (3 bistable circuits) showing both complement and reset lines, and an input pulse source. Use PNP transistors.

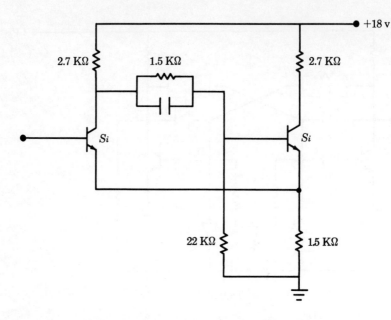

Figure 4-53.   Circuit for Problem 4.15.

4.17. Draw a schematic diagram showing how an astable blocking oscillator may be used as a pulse source for a monostable multivibrator.

4.18. Why is it impossible to saturate the transistor in a common base circuit arrangement?

4.19. How would you supply synchronizing pulses to an astable blocking oscillator?

4.20. Which form of monostable blocking oscillator may be triggered at a higher rate: the common emitter or the common base? (Assume identical transformers in each circuit.)

CHAPTER 5

Special Semiconductor Switches

5-1   Introduction

In this chapter we will be concerned with those semiconductor devices whose design and special characteristics make them ideally suited for use in switching circuits. These are the *unijunction transistor* and the *tunnel diode*. With the exception of the tunnnel diode, the devices have been specifically designed for use as non-linear switching elements and pulse sources, and are not suitable for use as linear amplifiers.

5-2   Tunnel Diodes

A conventional junction diode has rectifying properties. These properties are the result of a fairly wide junction between the P and N sides of the diode (1,500– 2,000 Å)* and small concentration of donor and acceptor impurities. In order for majority charge carriers to cross from one side of the junction to another, a forward bias must be applied. If the

---

* ($\text{Å} = 10^{-8}$ cm)

diode is reverse biased, only minority charge carriers cross the junction unless the reverse bias is great enough to cause avalanche breakdown. The typical volt-ampere characteristic of a junction diode and the energy-band diagram of an unbiased P-N junction are illustrated in Figure 5-1. This illustration is provided so that we may be able to compare the characteristics of a junction diode with those of the tunnel diode.

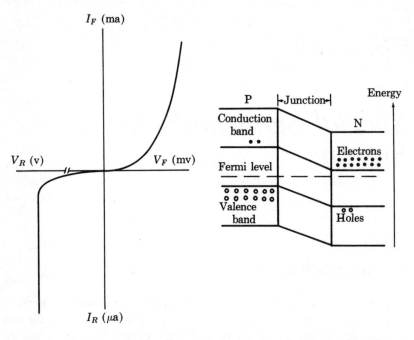

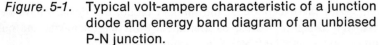

Figure. 5-1.   Typical volt-ampere characteristic of a junction diode and energy band diagram of an unbiased P-N junction.

The tunnel diode has **no** rectifying properties. Current flow will occur for either direction of bias voltage across the diode. As a matter of fact at certain voltages current flow in the reverse direction exceeds that of current flow in the forward-biased direction. The tunnel diode does exhibit a special property that makes it of value in switching and logic circuits. Over a small portion of the forward-biased characteristics of the tunnel diode, we are able to obtain a negative conductance region. When used as an amplifier, the tunnel diode is biased in the negative conductance region. However, for use as a switch it is operated on resistance stable regions on both sides of the negative conductance characteristic.

To understand the properties of the tunnel diode, we must first specify the physical properties and construction of the device. The tunnel diode is characterized by a very narrow junction between the P and N sides of the diode, usually about 150 Å. It is also necessary that there be such high concentrations of impurity atoms that the Fermi level will fall within the conduction band for the N side and within the valence band for the P side. An energy-band diagram of a tunnel diode is shown in Figure 5-2. The reader will recall that in a conventional P-N junction, a forward bias is needed in order that electrons in the conduction band of the N side of the diode acquire sufficient energy to "climb" the potential hill and cross over into the conduction band of the P side. There are several reasons for this: one, the valence band of the P.side of the junction contains very few un-occupied energy states; and two, the conduction band of the N side of the diode lies opposite the forbidden region, and there are no permitted energy states available to an electron within this region. In addition, the junction is wide, further decreasing the possibility that an electron might cross from the conduction band of the N side to the valence band of the P side. In the tunnel diode, the semiconductor material is so heavily doped that many holes are present in the P side. Therefore, there are unoccupied energy states for electrons in the valence band of the P side, and electrons in the conduction of the N side lying opposite each other. With the very narrow junction of the tunnel diode, electrons may cross from the conduction band of the N side into the valence band of the P side, without acquiring the needed energy to climb the hill from conduction band to conduction band.

When a tunnel diode is reverse biased, a greater portion of the conduction band of the N side lies opposite the valence band of the P side. Because

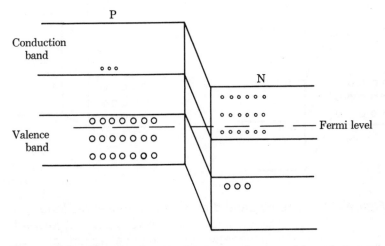

Figure. 5-2. Energy band diagram of an unbiased tunnel diode.

of the availability of energy states in the P side of the material, electrons enter the P side from the bias source, "tunnel" across the thin junction into the N side, and from there go to the positive terminal of the bias source. Because of the high impurity concentration, the diode simply behaves as a low resistance alloy. In addition, the reader is reminded that the reverse breakdown voltage of any junction diode is an inverse function of im-

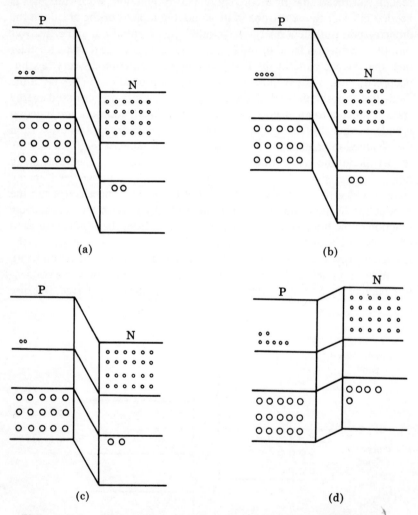

(a)

(b)

(c)

(d)

Figure. 5-3. Energy band diagrams of a tunnel diode for (a) reverse bias, (b) slight forward bias, (c) forward bias in negative conductance region, and (d) forward bias such that operation is the same as for a junction diode.

purity concentration. Because of the high impurity concentration of the tunnel diode, the reverse breakdown voltage approaches zero.

When a forward-bias voltage is applied to the tunnel diode, the conductance characteristic is initially the same as when the diode is reverse biased. However when the voltage across the diode reaches 25 to 50 millivolts, the *conductance* begins to *decrease*. This is due to the fact that the conduction band of the N side is now beginning to appear opposite the forbidden region, and less of the conduction band is located opposite the valence band of the P side. Further increasing the voltage across the diode causes *current to decrease*, since only a small portion of the conduction band of the N side is opposite the conduction band of the P side. Further increases in forward bias cause an increase in current flow. Now, the N-side conduction band is beginning to locate opposite the P-side conduction band, and from this point on the tunnel diode exhibits *V-I* properties similar to those of a junction diode. Figure 5-4 illustrates the volt-ampere characteristic of a typical tunnel diode. Figure 5-3 illustrates the energy-band diagrams of the tunnel diode for reverse bias, slight forward bias, forward bias in the negative conductance region, and forward bias such that operation is the same as for a junction diode.

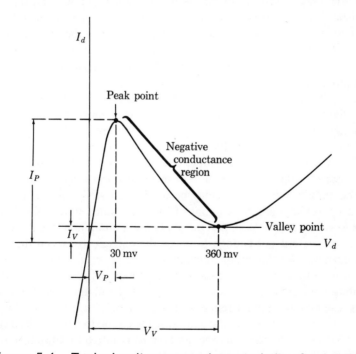

Figure. 5-4.   Typical volt-ampere characteristic of a tunnel
            diode.

5-3 Tunnel Diode Switching Circuits

The tunnel diode may be used in various forms of logic and multivibrator circuits. When used in bistable switching circuits, the tunnel diode possesses far greater speed than junction diodes or transistors. Theoretically, the limit on the mobility of charges in the tunnel diode approaches the speed of light. In actual practice, tunnel diodes have been used at frequencies in the order of 10^9 cycles per second. A tunnel diode may be arranged in a simple circuit to perform either OR or AND logic. The circuit for either logic function is of the same form. To perform OR logic, a load resistance is selected so that the load line intercepts the diode characteristic at two stable points. One of these points may then be referred to as 1 and the other as 0. The load should be selected so that an input at the terminals A or B will cause current to increase beyond the peak point. This will cause the diode to shift immediately to its other stable operating point. Figure 5-5 illustrates a simple threshold logic circuit and the load line of the circuit for use as an OR gate. In order for the circuit to perform OR logic, the circuit must switch between the two stable points on the characteristic. Let us refer to stable point a as the 0 state. This is the low voltage state of the diode and is the state of the circuit in the absence of any inputs. We shall refer to the 1 state of the circuit as stable point b. This stable state is a state of higher voltage and lower current than state a. An input pulse must be of sufficient amplitude to cause the load line to shift so that the load line intercepts the diode characteristic at only one point, c. When the input pulse is removed, the circuit does not revert back to 0; instead, the operating point shifts from c to b. This means that the circuit is bistable rather than monostable as in the transistor and junction diode OR gates. In order to cause the circuit to be at 0, so that it can be used again, it is necessary to supply a reset pulse or to remove the supply voltage.

The circuit of Figure 5-5 may be used as an AND gate. It becomes necessary to use a greater amount of load resistance so that the 0 point is at a lower current level. Upon the application of an input the diode current increases, but not enough to cause the current to exceed the peak-point current, and the circuit remains in its 0 state, a. When inputs are applied to both terminals, the diode current exceeds peak point, and the operating point immediately switches to point c; and upon the removal of inputs, the operating point remains at the stable point b representing a 1 output. Again, a reset is necessary to cause the circuit to revert to its 0 state. Figure 5-6 illustrates the load lines and inputs required to cause the circuit of Figure 5-5 to operate as an AND gate.

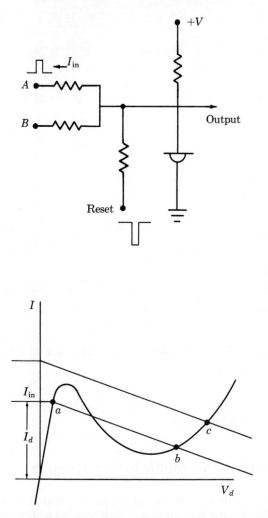

Figure 5-5.   Threshold logic circuit for use as an OR gate.

It should be apparent to the reader that the simple threshold circuit of Figure 5-5 offers several problems. First, the circuit is very sensitive to the amplitude of the input signals. This is not a serious problem for OR gates, but when the circuit is used as an AND gate, input levels must be carefully controlled. Certainly an AND gate with three inputs would be most unsuccessful if the circuit responded to only one or two inputs simply because one of the inputs happened to be larger than the circuit was designed to handle! In addition, the input and output terminals of the circuit

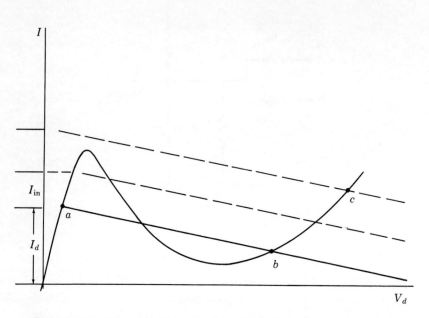

Figure 5-6. Threshold logic circuit load line when used as an AND gate.

are conductively coupled, and there is the possibility that input signals may appear at the output terminals.

5-4 Tunnel Diode Multivibrator Circuits

The tunnel diode may be used in any of the multivibrator forms by the proper choice of load line and operating bias. Figure 5-7 illustrates the typical tunnel diode characteristic with various load lines drawn on the characteristic. Load line I intercepts the characteristic only in the negative resistance region; thus, this operation would have no stable points, and would be the load line for operation of an astable multivibrator. Line II intercepts the characteristic at one stable point, and is correct operation for a monostable multivibrator. Load line III has two stable intercept points, and is obviously a bistable operation.

Figure 5-8 is the basic circuit of an astable multivibrator. When power is applied to the circuit, current rises gradually as a flux is established around the inductor. When the current reaches the peak-point value, the

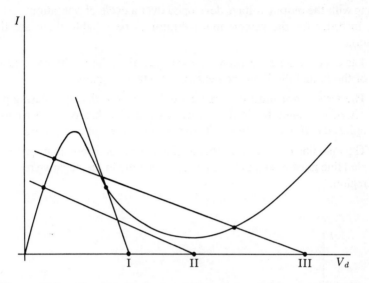

Figure 5-7. Tunnel diode load lines for astable, monostable, and bistable operation.

inductor prevents it from dropping. Because the inductor is now acting as a voltage source, the operating point of the circuit shifts to a high voltage level while holding the current at the peak-point level. At this time the voltage across the diode is greater than the supply voltage. The current then decreases to the valley point, at which time the circuit switches back into a low current, low voltage state. The cycle then repeats itself. The path of operation of the astable multivibrator is sketched in Figure 5-9. The cycle begins at point *a*, current rises to point *b*, remains at this level until the operation reaches point *c*, at which time current drops to point *d*. When the current reaches point *d* the voltage switches to point *a* and the cycle repeats.

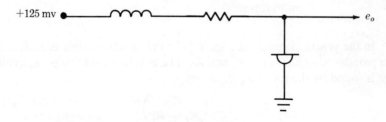

Figure 5-8. Basic circuit of an astable multivibrator.

A practical circuit of an astable multivibrator is shown in Figure 5-10, along with the output voltage developed over a cycle of operation.

In order for the astable multivibrator to be reliable there are three criteria:

1. The effective series resistance must be less than the minimum resistance of the tunnel diode in the negative resistance region.

2. The inductance must be large enough to insure that the biasing point will be unstable; that is, the inductance must be able to produce enough induced emf to cause the shift from point b to point c in Figure 5-9.

3. The load line must be such that astable operation is possible; that is, the load line must intercept the characteristic only in the negative resistance region.

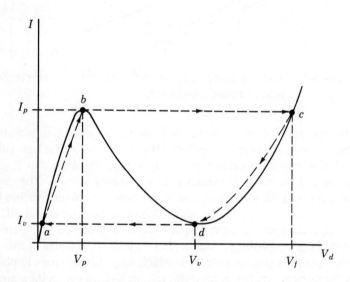

Figure 5-9.   Cycle of operation of the tunnel diode astable multivibrator.

In the practical circuit of Figure 5-10 the effective series resistance is the parallel combination of R_a and R_b. The effective load line source voltage is found by the following equation.

$$V_B = V_{BB} \left(\frac{R_b}{R_a + R_b} \right)$$ (5-1)

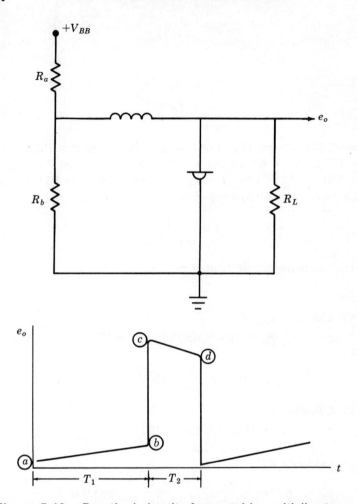

Figure 5-10.   Practical circuit of an astable multivibrator.

The time intervals T_1 and T_2 of Figure 5-10 may be found by the following approximations.

$$T_1 = \frac{L}{R_s + R_d'} \ln \frac{V_B - I_V(R_s + R_d')}{V_B - I_P(R_s + R_d')} \tag{5-2}$$

$$T_2 = \frac{L}{R_s + R_d''} \ln \frac{V_f + I_P R_s - V_B}{V_x + I_V R_s - V_B} \tag{5-3}$$

where:

$$R_d' = \frac{0.75\, V_P}{I_P} \tag{5-4}$$

$$R_d'' = \frac{V_f - V_x}{I_P - I_V} \tag{5-5}$$

$$V_x = \frac{V_f + V_V}{2} \tag{5-6}$$

Example 5.1.   In the circuit of Figure 5-10, assume that $V_{BB} = 4.5$ v, $R_a = 150\ \Omega$, $R_b = 6.8\ \Omega$, and $L = 92\ \mu h$. Assume that $V_P = 55$ mv, $V_V = 350$ mv, $I_P = 1$ ma, $I_V = 120\ \mu a$, and that $V_f = 500$ mv. Given that the free-running frequency of the astable multivibrator is

$$F = \frac{1}{T_1 + T_2}, \tag{5-7}$$

calculate the frequency of oscillations.

Solution:

(a) Calculate R_s.
$$R_s = 150 \times 6.8/156.8 = 6.52\ \Omega$$

(b) Calculate R_d'.
$$R_d' = \frac{0.75 \times 55 \times 10^{-3}}{10^{-3}} = 41.2\ \Omega$$

(c) Calculate V_x.
$$V_x = \frac{(350 + 500) \times 10^{-3}}{2} = 425\ \text{mv}$$

(d) Calculate R_d''.
$$R_d'' = \frac{(500 - 425) \times 10^{-3}}{(1 - 0.12) \times 10^{-3}} = 85.3\ \Omega$$

(e) Calculate V_B.
$$V_B = 4.5 \times \frac{6.8}{156.8} = 196\ \text{mv}$$

(f) Calculate T_1.
$$
\begin{aligned}
T_1 &= \frac{92 \times 10^{-6}}{6.52 + 41.2}\ \ln \frac{196 \times 10^{-3} - 0.12 \times 10^{-3}(6.52 + 41.2)}{196 \times 10^{-3} - 10^{-3}(6.52 + 41.2)} \\
&= \frac{92 \times 10^{-6}}{47.72}\ \ln \frac{190.3 \times 10^{-3}}{148.3 \times 10^{-3}} \\
&= 1.93 \times 10^{-6}\ \ln 1.283 \\
&= 1.93 \times 10^{-6} \times 0.249 = 0.481\ \mu\text{sec}
\end{aligned}
$$

(g) Calculate T_2.

$$T_2 = \frac{92 \times 10^{-6}}{6.52 + 85.3} \ln \frac{(500 + 6.52 - 196)(10^{-3})}{(425 + 0.12 \times 6.52 - 196)(10^{-3})}$$

$$= \frac{92 \times 10^{-6}}{91.82} \ln \frac{310.52 \times 10^{-3}}{230 \times 10^{-3}}$$

$$= 1.005 \times 10^{-6} \ln 1.36$$

$$= 1.005 \times 10^{-6} \times 0.308 = 0.309 \ \mu sec$$

(h) Calculate the frequency.

$$F = \frac{1}{(0.481 + 0.309)(10^{-6})} = 1.265 \ mc/s$$

Tunnel diode monostable multivibrators are similar to the astable circuit. The only difference is that the load line must intercept the diode characteristic at a stable point. The stable point may be to the left of the peak point (low voltage and current slightly less than peak-point current), or the operating point may be chosen to the right of the valley point (high voltage and current slightly greater than the valley current). Our first discussion will cover a monostable circuit whose stable operating point is to the left of the peak point. The load line for this circuit is drawn in Figure 5-11. All of the values of current and voltage needed for the equation of output pulse duration are shown in the figure.

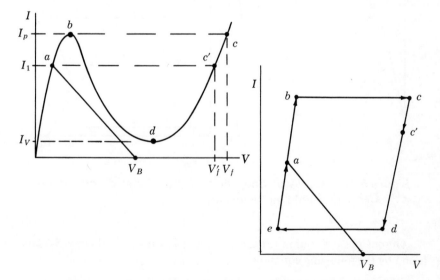

Figure 5-11. Cycle of operation of the tunnel diode monostable multivibrator.

The input trigger pulse to the circuit must be such that a current will be added to I_1 so that the diode current reaches peak point. Hence the input current must be $I_P - I_1$. Upon the application of the trigger pulse, the diode operating point shifts from a to b. Because of the instability at this point, the operating point immediately shifts from b to c. When the input trigger pulse is removed, the operating point shifts from c to c'. The current through the inductor then decreases exponentially until the valley-point current d is reached. The circuit then switches from d to e and then to the stable operating point a.

The duration of the output pulse is approximated by the following equation.

$$T = \frac{L}{R_s + R_d''} \ln \frac{V_f' + I_1 R_s - V_B}{V_x + I_V R_s - V_B} \qquad (5\text{-}8)$$

When monostable operation is obtained to the right of the valley point, the input trigger pulses must be negative. Figure 5-12 illustrates the load line and operation of the monostable multivibrator.

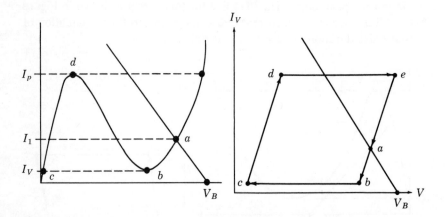

Figure 5-12.   Cycle of operation of the tunnel diode monostable multivibrator.

Output pulse duration for the operation illustrated in Figure 5-12 is found by the following equation.

$$T = \frac{L}{R_s + R_d'} \ln \frac{I_1(R_s + R_d') - V_B}{I_P(R_s + R_d') - V_B} \qquad (5\text{-}9)$$

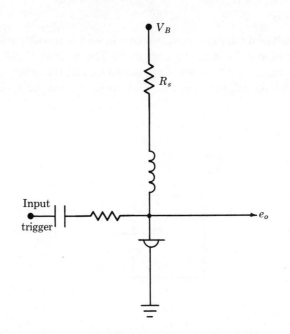

Figure 5-13. Tunnel diode monostable multivibrator.

The circuit for the monostable multivibrator is shown in Figure 5-13. The mode of operation is determined by the choice of V_B.

A tunnel diode bistable multivibrator is shown in Figure 5-14. The supply voltage is selected so that only one tunnel diode may be in a high voltage state at a given time. The operation of the circuit may be followed by first assuming a stable state. For example, we can assume that D_1 is in the 0 state and that D_2 is in the 1 state. Then

$$I_{D1} > I_{D2}$$

The inductor must then carry a current equal to

$$I_{D1} - I_{D2}$$

a. An input trigger pulse is applied. This causes D_1 to switch to the high voltage state. The inductor attempts to maintain a constant current flow. The polarity of the voltage across the inductor must therefore reverse. This induced emf subtracts from the input pulse and drives D_2 to a low voltage state.

b. As a result of the input trigger, we now have a new stable state. D_1 is in
the 1 state and D_2 is in the zero state. The normal direction of flow
through the inductor is now opposite to that of the other stable state.
When an input trigger is applied, D_2 is switched into the 1 state and the

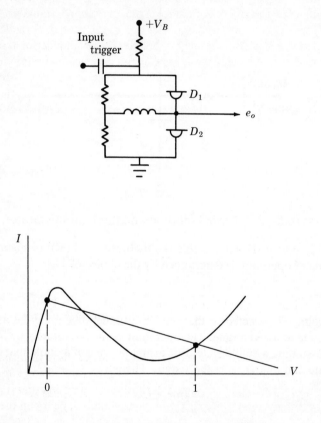

Figure 5-14.   Tunnel diode bistable multivibrator.

induced emf across the inductor drives D_1 into the 0 state. As in any bistable multivibrator, two trigger pulses are required to complete a cycle
of operation.

5-5   Unijunction Transistors

The unijunction transistor is a three-terminal device with but one junction. Two of the terminals are ohmic contacts, while the third is a rectifÿing junction. The UJT is constructed of either a bar or cube of N-type silicon. The rectifying contact is made by welding an aluminum wire to the silicon bar some distance from the other terminals. The bar type construction is most common and was the first of the practical UJT structures. Figure 5-15 is a sketch of the bar type of unijunction transistor. The terminals base 1 and base 2 are ohmic contacts. The rectifying contact is referred to as the emitter terminal. In effect we have a resistive voltage divider with the emitter junction located at some point along the length of the divider. In operation, base 2 is connected to a positive source and

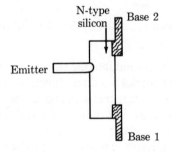

Figure 5-15.   Typical construction of a unijunction transistor.

base 1 is returned to ground. As a result of current flow from base 1 to base 2, there is a voltage gradient along the length of the silicon bar. Therefore, we have a voltage in the region of the emitter junction that is positive with respect to ground. Since this positive potential appears on the N side of the emitter, the emitter junction is back biased until the voltage between the emitter terminal and ground is sufficient to overcome the voltage between the N side of the emitter junction and ground. Effectively, we have a circuit consisting of two resistors and a junction diode. Analogous circuits of the UJT are often sketched in this manner. However, there is one important difference. When the emitter junction becomes forward biased, holes from the emitter are injected into the silicon bar. These holes travel from the emitter toward ground. As holes enter the silicon bar, elec-

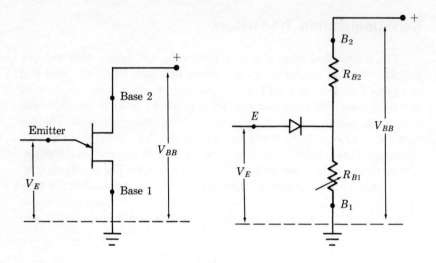

Figure 5-16.   Analogous circuit for the unijunction transistor.

trons are attracted from ground into the silicon bar. Since the conductivity of any semiconductor material is a direct function of the number of charge carriers per unit volume, this increase in charge carriers, when the emitter becomes forward biased, greatly reduces the resistance of the base 1 region. As the resistance of the base 1 region drops, so does the voltage across the region. As a result, emitter current rises while the voltage between the emitter terminal and ground decreases. Thus we have a *negative resistance* characteristic for the emitter over a certain range of emitter currents. The equivalent circuit of Figure 5-16 illustrates the analogy discussed above, but shows the base 1 resistor as a variable. The reason for the decreasing emitter voltage should be apparent. At any instant in time where the emitter junction is forward biased, the voltage from emitter to ground must always be the sum of the drop across the emitter junction and the drop from the region of the junction to the base 1 terminal. Since the drop across a silicon junction is approximately 0.7 volt (25°C) over a wide range of currents, we can approximate that

$$V_E = 0.7 + V_{RB1} \qquad\qquad \textbf{(5-10)}$$

At some point along the emitter current characteristic base 1 resistance rises again requiring an increase in emitter voltage in order to obtain an increase in emitter current. This will occur where the rate of hole injection is so great as to build a "positive space charge" in base 1 region. The great

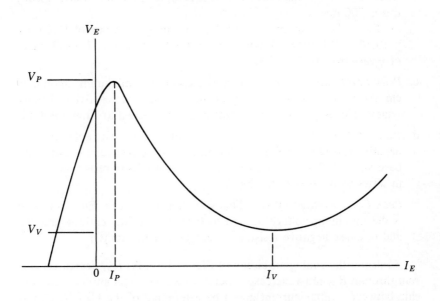

Figure 5-17. Volt-ampere emitter characteristic of the unijunction transistor.

utility of the unijunction transistor is due to the negative resistance portion
of the emitter characteristic. In Figure 5-17 we have the volt-ampere characteristic curve of the emitter junction showing both the peak points and
valley points of curve.

The emitter junction is in cutoff to the left of the peak point, and the
only emitter current flow is due to leakage current across the junction.
The negative resistance region exists between the peak point and the valley
point. At this point in our discussion we are now prepared to consider
some of the parameters of the unijunction transistor.

a. *Interbase Resistance* (R_{BB}). This is the resistance measured between
   the base 1 and base 2 contacts with the *emitter open*. R_{BB} is readily
   measured with a conventional ohmmeter. Typical values of R_{BB} vary
   from 4.7 to 9.1 kilohms.

b. *Intrinsic Standoff Ratio* (η). This parameter is determined by the
   location of the emitter junction with respect to base 1. If we define the
   voltage between the base terminals as V_{BB}, then η is most clearly defined by the following equation.

$$V_P = V_D + \eta V_{BB} \qquad \textbf{(5-11)}$$

where V_D is the voltage drop across the emitter-base junction. Typically this is 700 mv.

From the equation, we find that for any given value of V_{BB} for a particular UJT, the peak-point voltage is a function of η. Typical values of η vary from 0.47 to 0.82.

c. *Peak-Point Current (I_P).* This represents the minimum amount of emitter current required to trigger the UJT into its negative resistance region. This is the minimum emitter current needed to "fire" the UJT.

d. *Valley Current (I_V).* This is the maximum emitter current within the negative resistance region. Valley current is a direct function of inter-base voltage (V_{BB}) and an inverse function of any resistance that is in series with either of the bases.

e. *Peak-Point Voltage (V_P).* This voltage is defined by Eq. (5-11). It is the minimum voltage needed to forward bias the emitter junction and to cause negative resistance operation of the emitter.

Consider the analogous circuit of Figure 5-16. As R_{B1} decreases, current through R_{B2} must increase. Therefore we have still another relationship between emitter current and a base terminal of the UJT. It is possible for us to vary the base-2 current by the emitter current. This is defined as the *Interbase Modulated Current ($I_{B2\text{-mod}}$).* This parameter is the effective current gain between I_E and I_{B2}. This effect of emitter current upon I_{B2} is illustrated in Figure 5-18.

It is not intended that this chapter include a complete UJT manual. The literature is replete with examples of operation of the unijunction transistor in industrial applications. It is our purpose to examine the uses of the UJT in switching circuits of the nature discussed in previous chapters of this text. However, nearly all applications of the UJT use some form of relaxation oscillator. Before we proceed to use the UJT as a multivibrator or in hybrid timing circuits, we shall follow the operation of the basic relaxation oscillator.

A unijunction relaxation oscillator is shown in Figure 5-19. Here the voltage that will exceed peak point is obtained across the capacitor. The emitter is back biased until the charge on the capacitor exceeds peak-point voltage. When this occurs, the emitter junction fires and the capacitor discharges through the emitter and base-1 circuits. When the voltage across the capacitor drops to $V_{E(\text{min})}$, the emitter junction becomes reverse biased, the discharge stops, and another cycle begins.

The frequency of the circuit of Figure 5-19 is determined by the time required for C_1 to reach peak-point voltage.

$$V_P = \eta V_{BB} + V_D \approx \eta V_{BB}$$

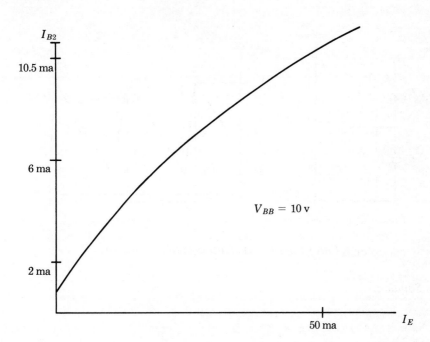

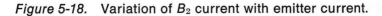

Figure 5-18. Variation of B_2 current with emitter current.

Substituting V_{BB} for the charge on the capacitor, and using the standard equation for the charge of a capacitor, we have:

$$\eta V_{BB} = V_{BB}(1 - \epsilon^{-t/R_1 C_1})$$
$$\eta = 1 - \epsilon^{-t/R_1 C_1}$$
$$\epsilon^{-t/R_1 C_1} = 1 - \eta$$
$$\epsilon^{t/R_1 C_1} = \frac{1}{1 - \eta}$$
$$t = R_1 C_1 \ln \frac{1}{1 - \eta}$$
$$f = \frac{1}{R_1 C_1 \ln \dfrac{1}{1 - \eta}} \tag{5-12}$$

Example 5.2. A type 2N2422B unijunction transistor is to be used as a sawtooth-wave generator. Using the circuit of Figure 5-19, what is the approximate frequency of the relaxation oscillator if the intrinsic standoff ratio is 0.7, $R_1 = 270$ KΩ, and $C_1 = 0.002$ μfd?

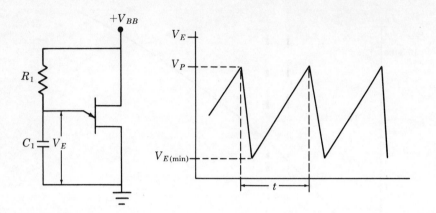

Figure 5-19.   UJT relaxation oscillator.

Solution:

$$f = \cfrac{1}{R_1 C_1 \ln \cfrac{1}{1 - \eta}}$$

$$= \cfrac{1}{270 \times 10^3 \times 2 \times 10^{-9} \ln \cfrac{1}{0.3}}$$

$$= \frac{1}{540 \times 10^{-6} \ln 3.33} = 1.54 \text{ kc/s}$$

The load line of the circuit of Figure 5-19 has a slope that is equal to the reciprocal of R_1. The load line must intercept the negative resistance characteristic between the peak point and the valley point. This insures that there will be sufficient emitter current to fire the UJT and also makes certain that the emitter junction is held out of saturation, so that the UJT will turn off at the end of the cycle. The voltage $V_{E(min)}$ in Figure 5-19 is typically 0.6 of the valley voltage.

The circuit of Figure 5-19 supplies a sawtooth voltage at the emitter terminal. Since there is a change in both base 1 and base 2 currents when the emitter junction becomes forward biased, pulse voltages may be obtained if the basic circuit is modified. The modified circuit is shown in Figure 5-20. A negative pulse is available at base 2 and a positive pulse at base 1.

The frequency of oscillations is found in the same manner as for the basic circuit. When R_2 and R_3 are negligible in comparison to R_{BB}, Eq.

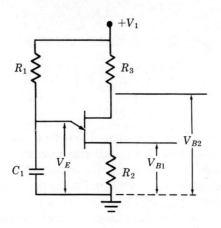

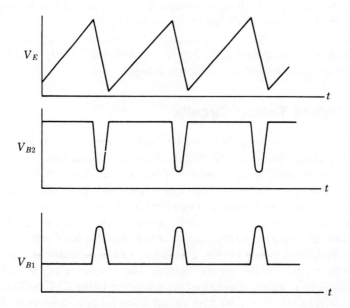

Figure 5-20.   UJT relaxation oscillator producing positive
and negative pulses and sawtooth waves.

(5-12) may be used. A more accurate result is obtained if R_2 and R_3 are
included in the computation of the time required for C_1 to charge to peak-
point voltage.

$$V_P = V_1 \left(\frac{R_2 + \eta R_{BB}}{R_2 + R_3 + R_{BB}} \right)$$

$$V_1 \left(\frac{R_2 + \eta V_{BB}}{R_2 + R_3 + R_{BB}} \right) = V_1 (1 - \epsilon^{-t/R_1 C_1})$$

$$t = R_1 C_1 \ln \left(\frac{1}{1 - \dfrac{R_2 + \eta R_{BB}}{R_2 + R_3 + R_{BB}}} \right)$$

$$f = 1/t \tag{5-13}$$

The unijunction relaxation oscillator may be further modified to produce an output at the base 2 terminal that resembles the output of an astable multivibrator. For this reason the circuit when so arranged is referred to as an unijunction multivibrator. During the period of time needed for C_1 to charge to V_P, V_{B2}, the voltage at base 2 is high and the UJT is in its OFF condition. The capacitor charges through the diode and R_1. OFF time is controlled by R_1 and C. When the peak point is reached, the UJT is ON, the capacitor discharges through R_2 and the emitter-to-base-1 circuit of the UJT. Hence ON time is controlled by R_2 and C_1. During ON time the voltage at base 2 is reduced. These controlled ON and OFF periods produce an output at the base 2 terminal that is fairly rectangular. The circuit and waveforms are shown in Figure 5-21.

5-6 Hybrid Timing Circuits

The unijunction transistor may be used in conjunction with conventional transistor bistable multivibrators to provide circuit functions similar to those of the astable multivibrator. However, the conventional astable multivibrator has an output voltage that is not truly rectangular because of the charging currents flowing through the load resistors. A bistable multivibrator has an output more nearly approaching the ideal rectangular wave, *provided that the bistable circuit is switched at a fixed rate.*

In the hybrid timing circuit, a UJT relaxation oscillator is used as a source of trigger for the bistable circuit. The frequency of the "astable multivibrator" is simply one-half of the frequency of the UJT oscillator. In Figure 5-22, a self-biased bistable circuit using NPN transistors is shown with a typical UJT relaxation oscillator. The frequency of oscillations of the UJT is readily found by use of Figure 5-13. The frequency of the square-wave output is then one-half the frequency of the UJT oscillator.

In the design of the circuit shown in Figure 5-22, the bistable circuit is designed in accordance with the techniques covered in Chapter 4. By adding the UJT to the circuit, the resistor R_2 becomes part of the total emitter circuit resistance of the bistable circuit. It is common practice to

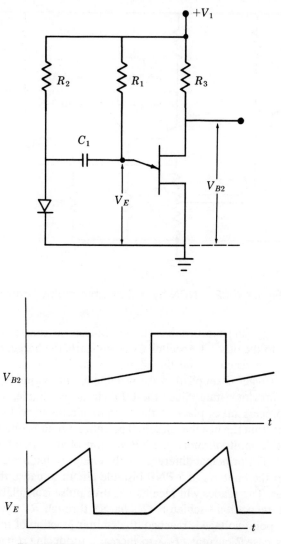

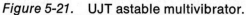

Figure 5-21. UJT astable multivibrator.

make R_2 very much smaller than R_E. The explanation of the circuit is very straightforward. C_1 charges through R_1. Until the charge on C_1 reaches the peak-point voltage, the bistable circuit is in one of its stable states. When the charge on C_1 reaches peak point, the emitter junction of the UJT fires. The discharge current of C_1 develops a positive pulse

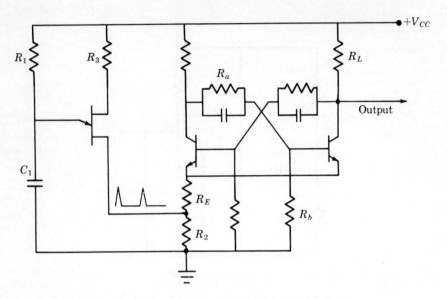

Figure 5-22.   NPN hybrid astable multivibrator.

across R_2 triggering the bistable circuit, causing a transistion from one stable state to the other. Capacitor C_1 again starts to charge. When peak-point voltage is reached, and the emitter of the UJT again fires and discharges C_1, trigger is supplied to the bistable circuit, switching the circuit back to its previous state. Since the UJT circuit is astable, a continuous switching process takes place in the bistable circuit providing a square-wave output from the bistable circuit. The entire circuit is referred to as an **hybrid astable multivibrator.** A PNP version of the circuit is shown in Figure 5-23. The principal difference in the circuit is that a negative trigger is needed at the emitters of a PNP bistable circuit to cause the circuit to switch states. The reader will recall a negative pulse is available at base 2 of the UJT relaxation oscillator. C_1 charges through R_1 towards $|V_{cc}|$. When peak-point voltage is reached, the emitter junction of the UJT fires. This causes base 2 current (I_{B2}) to increase, producing a negative pulse across R_3' switching the bistable circuit. Once again, R_3' is selected to be much smaller than R_E.

The circuits of Figures 5-22 and 5-23 are symmetrical astable hybrid multivibrators. Where a non-symmetrical rectangular wave is desired, the circuit can be modified so as to provide two separate charging paths for C_1. A non-symmetrical astable circuit is illustrated in Figure 5-24. The charging circuit for C_1 depends upon the particular stable state of the

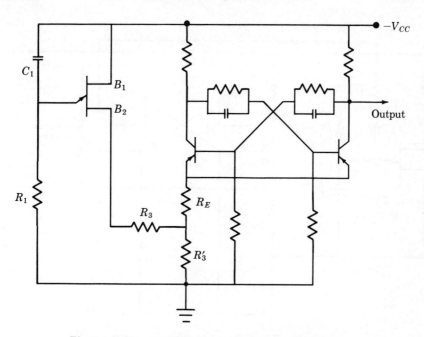

Figure 5-23.   PNP hybrid astable multivibrator.

bistable circuit. If we assume that Q_1 is in cutoff and Q_2 is in saturation, then C_1 charges through R_1. The time required for C_1 to reach peak-point voltage is then controlled by $R_1 C_1$. When peak-point voltage is reached and a positive trigger is developed across the resistor R_2, the circuit switches stable states. Q_1 is now in saturation, and Q_2 is in cutoff. C_1 now charges through R_1', and the time needed for C_1 to charge to peak-point voltage is now controlled by $R_1' C_1$. Since R_1 and R_1' may be entirely different, the output waveform is now non-symmetrical.

Example 5.3.   Design an hybrid astable multivibrator circuit with a square-wave output. The output waveform is to have a peak-to-peak amplitude of 25 v at a frequency of 400 cps. The semiconductor components have the following characteristics.

Unijunction transistor: Intrinsic standoff ratio $= 0.62$
                              Interbase resistance $R_{BB} = 5100 \ \Omega$

Transistors: NPN
$$V_{CE(\text{max})} = 50 \text{ v}$$
$$I_{C(\text{max})} \ \ = 125 \text{ ma}$$
$$h_{FE(\text{min})} = 18$$

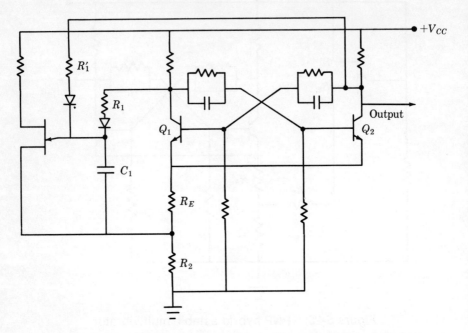

Figure 5-24. NPN hybrid astable with asymmetrical timing intervals.

Solution:

(a) Design a self-biased bistable multivibrator as outlined in Chapter 4.

 (1) Select $V_{CC} = 30$ v.

 (2) Let $V_E = 5$ v. (This choice is made so that the output will swing from $+5$ to $+30$ v, therefore supplying a 25-v peak-to-peak output voltage.)

 (3) Let $I_{C(\text{sat})} = 20$ ma.

 (4) $R_E + R_L = \dfrac{V_{CC}}{I_{C(\text{sat})}}$ [Eq. (4-12)]
 $= 1500\ \Omega$

 (5) Solve for R_E.

$$\frac{R_E}{R_E + R_L} = \frac{V_E}{V_{CC}}$$
$$R_E = 250\ \Omega$$

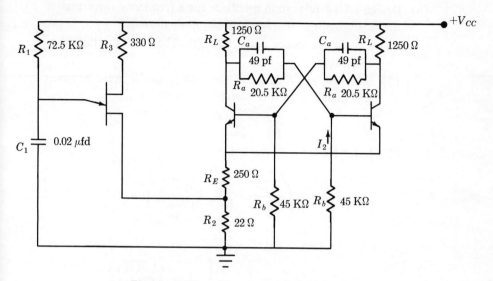

Figure 5-25. Circuit for Example 5.3.

(6) $R_L = 1500 - R_E = 1250 \ \Omega$

(7) Solve for I_B.

$$I_B = \frac{V_{CC}}{(R_E + R_L)h_{FE(min)}} \qquad \text{[Eq. (4-19)]}$$

$$= \frac{30}{1500 \times 18} = 1.11 \ \text{ma}$$

(8) Let I_2 equal 0.1 I_B. (See Figures 4-23 and 5-25.)

$$I_2 = 111 \ \mu\text{a}$$

(9) Solve for R_b. (See Figure 5-25.)

$$R_b = \frac{V_E}{I_2} \qquad \text{[Eq. (4-14)]}$$

$$= \frac{5}{0.111 \times 10^{-3}} = 45 \ \text{K}\Omega$$

(10) Solve for R_a. (See Figure 5-25.)

$$R_a = \frac{V_{CC} - V_E}{I_B + I_2} \qquad \text{[Eq. (4-15)]}$$

$$= \frac{25}{1.22 \times 10^{-3}} = 20.5 \ \text{K}\Omega$$

(11) Solve for C_a. (See Figure 5-25.)

$$C_a = \frac{10^{-6}}{R_a} = \frac{10^{-6}}{0.205 \times 10^5} = 49 \ \text{pf}$$

(b) Design a UJT relaxation oscillator for a frequency *twice* that of the desired output frequency of the multivibrator.

    (1) Let the frequency equal 800 cps. Therefore the time $t = 1.25$ msec.

    (2) Select R_3 and R_2. R_3 can vary widely, but R_2 must be much less than R_E. In this example we shall let

$$R_3 = 330 \ \Omega$$
$$R_2 = 22 \ \Omega$$

    (3) Solve Eq. (5-13) for $R_1 C_1$.

$$R_1 C_1 = t \ \cfrac{1}{\ln\left(\cfrac{1}{1 - \cfrac{R_2 + \eta R_{BB}}{R_2 + R_3 + R_{BB}}}\right)}$$

$$= 1.25 \times 10^{-3} \times \cfrac{1}{\ln\left(\cfrac{1}{1 - \cfrac{22 + 0.62 \times 5100}{22 + 330 + 5100}}\right)}$$

$$= 1.25 \times 10^{-3} \times \frac{1}{\ln 2.36}$$

$$= 1.25 \times 10^{-3} \times \frac{1}{0.86} = 1.45 \times 10^{-3}$$

    (4) Let $C_1 = 0.02 \ \mu$fd. (This is entirely an arbitrary choice; we could have selected any value such that R_1 would be some value between 3000 Ω and 1 megohm.)

    (5) Solve for R_1.

$$R_1 = \frac{2.9 \times 10^{-3}}{0.02 \times 10^{-6}} = 72.5 \ \text{K}\Omega$$

(c) The completed circuit is shown in Figure 5-25.

Example 5.4. Use the same semiconductor components as in Example 5.3. Design an hybrid astable circuit with a peak-to-peak output of 25 v, a frequency of 500 cps, and an output waveform as shown in Figure 5-26.

Solution:

(a) Use the same techniques and same values as in Example 5.3 for the bistable multivibrator portion of the hybrid circuit.

$$R_E = 250 \ \Omega \qquad R_a = 20.5 \ \text{pf K}\Omega$$
$$R_L = 1250 \ \Omega \qquad C_a = 49 \ \text{pf}$$
$$R_b = 45 \ \text{K}\Omega$$

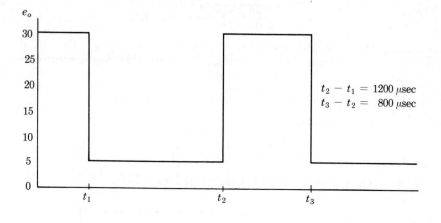

Figure 5-26.   Output waveform for Example 5.4.

(b) Design the UJT relaxation oscillator for two different time periods.

(1) Select R_3 and R_2 as in Example 5.3.

$$R_2 = 22 \ \Omega \qquad R_3 = 330 \ \Omega$$

(2) Solve Eq. (5-13) for R_1C_1.

$$R_1C_1 = t \frac{1}{\ln\left(\cfrac{1}{1 - \cfrac{R_2 + \eta R_{BB}}{R_2 + R_3 + R_{BB}}}\right)}$$

(3) The time interval $t_2 - t_3$ of the output wave is developed during the period that Q_2 is in cutoff. This period is the time that C_1 is charged through R'_1 of Figure 5-24. Use this value of time in the equation derived in step (2), and solve for R'_1C_1.

$$R'_1C_1 = 8 \times 10^{-4} \times \frac{1}{\ln\left(\cfrac{1}{1 - \cfrac{22 \times 0.62 \times 5100}{22 + 330 + 5100}}\right)}$$

$$= 8 \times 10^{-4} \times \frac{1}{\ln 2.36}$$

$$= 8 \times 10^{-4} \times 1.16 = 9.26 \times 10^{-4}$$

(4) Let $C_1 = 0.05 \ \mu\text{fd}$

(5) Solve for R'_1.

$$R'_1 = \frac{9.26 \times 10^{-4}}{0.05 \times 10^{-6}} = 18.5 \text{ K}\Omega$$

(6) The time interval $t_1 - t_2$ of the output wave is the period for which Q_1 is in cutoff. This timing interval is controlled by R_1C_1. Solve for R_1C_1.

$$R_1C_1 = 12 \times 10^{-4} \times 1.16 = 13.9 \times 10^{-4}$$

(7) Solve for R_1.

$$R_1 = \frac{13.9 \times 10^{-4}}{0.05 \times 10^{-6}} = 26.8 \text{ K}\Omega$$

(c) The completed circuit is shown in Figure 5-27.

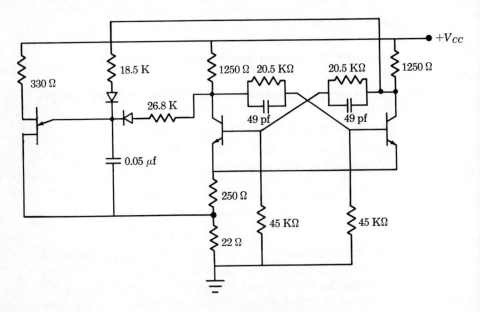

Figure 5-27. Circuit for Example 5.4.

PROBLEMS

5.1. In the circuit of Figure 5-25, $R_1 = 56 \text{ K}\Omega$ and $R_E = 470 \, \Omega$. All other component values are as in the figure. Plot a graph of output voltage versus time for 1½ cycles of output.

5.2. Will a change in the amount of collector supply voltage change the frequency of the output in the circuit of Figure 5-25? Explain.

5.3. Given the following data:

     Transistors: PNP

$$V_{CE(max)} = -35 \text{ v.}$$
$$I_{C(max)} = 75 \text{ ma}$$
$$h_{FE(min)} = 40$$

     Unijunction transistor: $R_{BB} = 6200 \text{ } \Omega$
$$\eta = 0.68$$

Design an hybrid circuit for symmetrical output with a frequency of 2000 cps and an output voltage swing from -30 to -10 v.

5.4. Use the semiconductor parameters of Example 5-3. Design a symmetrical hybrid astable circuit to develop a 150-cps output with a peak-to-peak swing of 15 v. Let $V_{CC} = 18$ v and $I_{C(sat)} = 25$ ma.

5.5. Design an hybrid astable circuit to produce the output waveform shown in Figure 5-28. Use the semiconductor parameters of Problem 5.3.

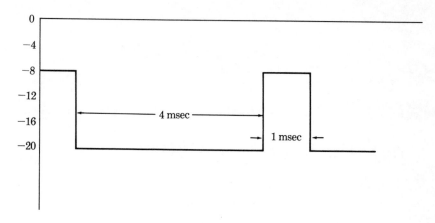

Figure 5-28. Output waveform for Problem 5.5.

5.6. In the circuit of Example 5.4, change R_1 to 10 KΩ. Plot a graph of output voltage versus time for two cycles of operation.

5.7. In the circuit of Figure 5-20, $R_2 = 75 \text{ } \Omega$, $R_3 = 560 \text{ } \Omega$, $R_1 = 120 \text{ K}\Omega$, and $C_1 = 0.03 \text{ } \mu\text{fd}$. Let $R_{BB} = 7000 \text{ } \Omega$ and $\eta = 0.71$. Solve for the frequency of the relaxation oscillator.

5.8. Redesign the circuit of Problem 5.7 so that the frequency is 270 cps. The problem has two solutions. (a) Solve for a new value of R_1 while leaving C_1 unchanged. (b) Solve for a new value C_1 while leaving R_1 unchanged.

5.9. In the circuit of Figure 5-10, what is the frequency of the tunnel diode multivibrator if $L = 65$ μh? Use the circuit components and parameters of Example 5.1.

5.10. Explain what is meant by *Fermi level*.

CHAPTER 6

Applications

6-1 Introduction

In this chapter we shall make use of the material studied in the preceding chapters. The applications of logic and regenerative switching will be stated as problems requiring solutions. Although we shall attempt several solutions to most of the problems, it is earnestly hoped that the reader will arrive at additional solutions for these problems.

6-2 Counters

Saturated or non-saturated bistable multivibrators may be used for counting. Because the bistable circuit has two stable states, its usage with binary coded numbers is simple and logical.

Saturated bistable multivibrators are used in industrial counters, scintillation recorders, and other applications where high speed operation is not required. The non-saturated types are used in digital computers and other applications where the storage time delay caused by saturation must be avoided.

The circuits of any counter must have symmetrical triggering in order to advance the count, and non-symmetrical triggering for reset purposes. The number of bistable multivibrators in the counter is determined by the size of the numbers to be handled. Equation (6-1) may be used to deter-

151

mine the number of bistable circuits needed to handle a particular *decimal*
number.

$$n = \frac{\log_{10} Y}{0.301} \qquad \text{(6-1)}$$

where n = number of bistable multivibrators

Y = decimal number to be counted.

A block diagram of a binary counter is shown in Figure 6-1. Input
pulses are available only to B_0; reset pulses are applied to all of the bistable
multivibrators simultaneously. The bistable circuits represent the various
powers of 2. B_0 represents 2^0, B_1 represents 2^1, B_2 represents 2^2, and B_3
represents 2^3. Since this counter consists of just these four stages, the highest number the counter can contain when all of the bistable circuits are at
1 is 15. (Binary 15 = 1111). A sixteenth input pulse to this counter would
cause all of the bistables to be set to 0.

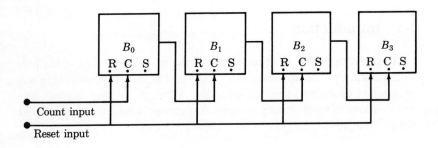

Figure 6-1. Block diagram of a binary counter.

The circuits of the counter must be interconnected in such a manner
that when B_0 switches from 0 to 1, the resultant output pulse from B_0 cannot cause B_1 to switch. B_1 will switch from 0 to 1 *only when B_0 switches
from 1 to 0.* In a similar manner, B_1 must switch B_2 from 0 to 1 only when
B_1 switches from 1 to 0; and B_3 switches from 0 to 1 only when B_2
switches from 1 to 0. The reader will recall that with the use of steering
circuits and symmetrical triggering, a bistable multivibrator can be made
to respond to either positive or negative pulses, but not to both. The transistor in the output side of each bistable circuit is in saturation when the
multivibrator is in the 0 state. Switching the circuit to 1 causes the transistor to go into cutoff. The change in voltage at the collector (negative
with PNP transistors and positive with NPN transistors) is coupled to the
symmetrical input point of the next bistable, but is of the *wrong* polarity

to cause a change of states. When the bistable circuit is switched back to 0, a pulse of proper polarity is transferred to the next bistable circuit and causes it to change states.

If we assume that the transistors in the counter of Figure 6-1 are PNP, then the voltage changes at the collectors are from 0 to $-V_{CC}$ when a bistable switches from 0 to 1, and from $-V_{CC}$ to 0 when it switches from 1 to 0. The correct polarity of trigger to a PNP bistable circuit is positive. This trigger is obtained when V_{CE} changes from $-V_{CC}$ to 0. Hence, a correct trigger output to the next bistable is had when a bistable multivibrator changes from 1 to 0.

Figure 6-2 illustrates the output voltage levels of the bistable circuits of Figure 6-1 for input pulses from 0 through 16. The reader will observe that the counter is "filled" at 15 and resets with the 16th pulse.

Example 6.1. Design a counter using PNP transistors. The counter will handle numbers up to 32 and is to be used for low speed applications.

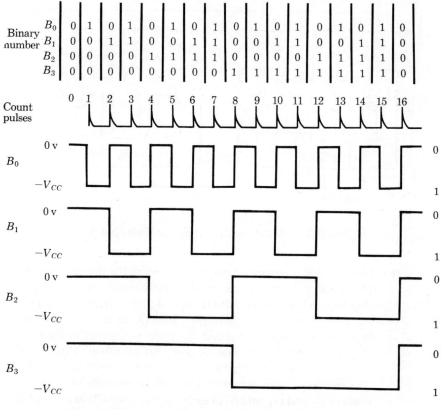

Figure 6-2. Voltage changes in a binary counter.

Solution:

  (a) Determine the number of bistable multivibrators needed.
By use of Eq. (6-1), $n = 5$.

  (b) The next step in the design of any counter is to decide upon how
the various bistable circuits are to be interconnected.

     (1) As a first solution to the problem, let us use base triggering
with steering diodes for the symmetrical trigger input. The
triggering circuit will be arranged so as to respond only to
positive pulses.

     (2) The reset pulse line must be arranged so that the output side
transistors are in saturation when the counter is reset. This
can be done by supplying an OFF pulse to each of the other
transistors in the counter. Therefore the reset pulse will be
a positive pulse.

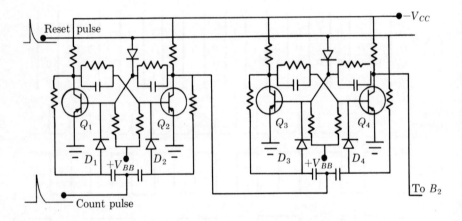

Figure 6-3.   Binaries B_0 and B_1 for Example 6.1.

  (c) Figure 6-3 is a schematic diagram of two of the bistable circuits
(B_0 and B_1) showing the method of interconnection discussed in
step (b). When a reset pulse is applied to the circuit, Q_1 and Q_3
are driven into cutoff, causing Q_2 and Q_4 to be in saturation.
When a count pulse is applied, the pulse is directed to the base
of Q_2 by D_2. Q_2 cuts off, and Q_1 goes into saturation. This results
in a negative pulse applied to the symmetrical input point of B_1.
The steering circuit prevents this pulse from appearing at the
bases of Q_3 and Q_4, and B_1 does not switch states. When the next
count pulse is applied, B_0 again changes states. Q_1 is driven into

cutoff, and Q_2 into saturation. The output voltage now changes from $-V_{CC}$ to 0, and a positive pulse is coupled to B_1. D_4 directs this pulse to the base of Q_4, driving it into cutoff and Q_3 into saturation. At this instant, a negative pulse is obtained in the output of B_1. This pulse cannot affect B_2. The pulse count is now 2, and the binary counter reads 10. The third input pulse switches B_0 to 1. This causes Q_2 to go into cutoff and sends a negative pulse to B_1. But B_1 will not switch when a negative pulse is applied and, therefore, remains in the 1 state. The pulse count is now 3, and the binary counter reads 11. In exactly the same manner, B_1 is connected to B_2; B_2 to B_3; and B_3 to B_4.

(d) The individual bistable multivibrators are designed in accordance with the principles covered in Chapter 4.

(e) The essential circuit is shown in Figure 6-4. The cross-coupling circuits have been omitted so that the reader can concentrate on the reset and coupling circuits.

The coupling of the bistable circuits of the counter could have been done by the use of a common load resistor as shown in Figure 4-36. Negative pulse output from one bistable to another cannot cause switching.

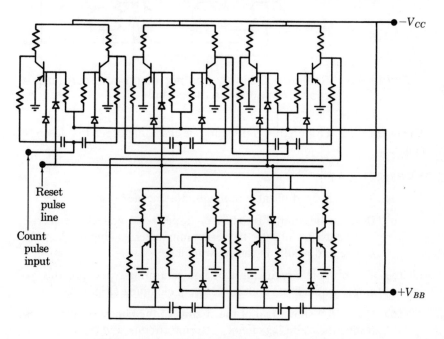

Figure 6-4. Scale-of-32 binary counter.

However, a positive pulse from B_0 to B_1 causes both transistors of B_1 to cut off. The charges on the commutating capacitors of B_1 will then cause B_1 to change states when the pulse is removed. Reset can be accomplished as in Figure 6-3. The circuit is shown in Figure 6-5.

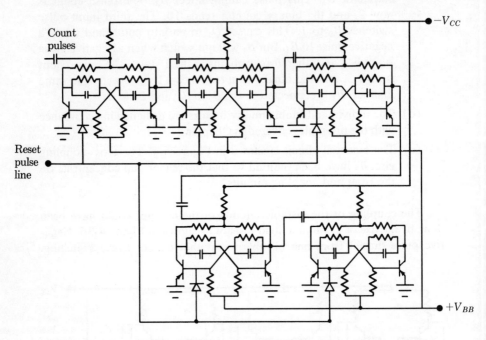

Figure 6-5. Scale-of-32 binary counter using common load resistor to advance the count.

Example 6.2. Using NPN transistors, design a high-speed scale-of-16 counter.

Solution:

(a) The number of bistable multivibrators needed is 4.

(b) Because the counter is to be a high speed one, collector triggering is to be used. Collector triggering minimizes loading on the pulse source and results in faster switching.

(c) The bistable circuits must be non-saturating types. For this example we shall use collector current clamping (Figure 2-15).

(d) Figure 6-6 shows two of the circuits of the binary counter, illustrating the clamping circuits, steering circuits, and reset input.

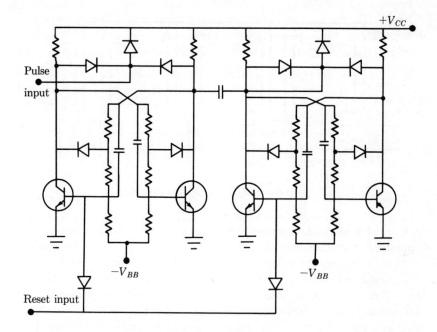

Figure 6-6.   Non-saturating bistable multivibrators as used in
              a binary counter.

The speed of any counter can be increased if we use AND gates to sense the states of the bistable multivibrators. In this manner trigger pulses are fed from bistable to bistable without the need for the time required for the bistable circuit to switch from 1 to 0. A block diagram of a scale-of-16 counter is shown in Figure 6-7.

The reader will note that in this type of counter the count pulse is applied to the first bistable unit and to the first AND gate. If the bistable multivibrator is in the 0 state, the AND gate does not produce an output to the next bistable circuit. However, the first circuit now switches from 0 to 1. When the next count pulse is applied, the AND gate produces an output because both inputs to the AND gate are at 1. This provides a trigger to the complement input of the next bistable circuit, causing it to switch. At the same time, the first bistable circuit switches from 1 to 0. When the third count pulse is applied, the first bistable circuit again switches to 1. However, the AND gate associated with the first bistable does not produce an output, because the bistable was at 0 when the count pulse was applied. In a similar manner the count proceeds from one cir-

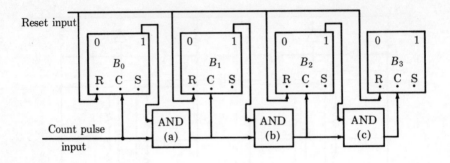

Figure 6-7.   Gated binary counter.

cuit to the next. Aside from the increase in speed of operation, the counter operates in the same manner as the other counter discussed in this section.

Let us pick up the action of the counter at various points. Assume that the count is 6, binary 0110. When the seventh pulse is applied, B_0 switches from 0 to 1, and AND gate (a) provides no output trigger pulse to B_1. The count is now 7, binary 0111. When the eighth pulse is applied, AND gate (a) operates, providing trigger pulses to B_1 and to AND gate (b). Bistable B_0 switches to 0. AND gate (b) operates, causing an output trigger to be supplied to B_2 and to AND gate (c). Because of the trigger pulse from AND gate (a), B_1 switches to 0; and because AND gate (b) provided trigger to B_2, it also switches to 0. The output of AND gate (c) switches B_3 to 1. The count is now 1000, which is binary equivalent of 8.

It is possible that a "race" problem will occur with this type of counter. That is, a bistable circuit may switch states before the AND gate connected to its 1 output terminal can operate. To prevent this problem, delay lines may be introduced between the 1 output terminal of the bistable multivibrator and the AND gate. These delay lines usually are small sections of artificial transmission line. The delay inserted by these lines is still less than the delay caused by waiting for a bistable circuit to switch states in order to transfer a trigger to the next bistable multivibrator. The circuit of Figure 6-8 illustrates the details of a gated counter.

The bistable multivibrators shown in Figure 6-8 are non-saturating, using diodes D_1, D_2, D_3, and D_4 to keep the transistors out of saturation. The circuits use hybrid triggering, with D_5 and D_6 as steering diodes. The important part of the circuit is the gating method used to supply trigger to the next bistable circuit. From the diagram, it is apparent that we are looking at B_0 and B_1. When B_0 is in its 0 state, diode D_7 is forward biased, holding the diode AND gate's output at a low level, keeping Q_4 in cutoff.

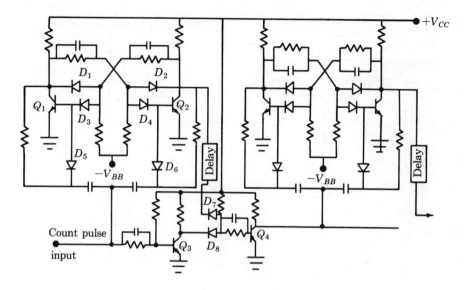

Figure 6-8. Circuits for a gated binary counter.

When a count pulse is applied, Q_3 cuts off; but because D_7 remains forward biased, Q_4 cannot come on, preventing the transfer of a trigger pulse to B_1. However, the count pulse does cause B_0 to switch from 0 to 1. This causes V_{CE} for Q_2 to be high, effectively reverse biasing D_7. When a count pulse is applied, driving Q_3 into cutoff, the output of the diode AND gate switches from some very low voltage to a high positive voltage, turning on Q_4. When Q_4 comes on, its collector voltage drops, causing it to switch states. The reader will note that the gating circuit is fairly complex. However, a combination of transistors and a diode AND gate is not the only solution to the problem. An all-transistorized AND gate may be used. Such a circuit is shown in Figure 6-9. The counter is not shown; only the circuitry necessary to follow the operation of the AND gate is illustrated. So long as either transistor of the gate is conducting, there is some high positive voltage available across the load terminals of the gate. When both transistors are cut off, the output voltage will drop to zero, providing a negative trigger for the next bistable circuit.

It should be noted that in the AND gate, we are driving the base of Q_3 from the collector of Q_1. The reader will recall that the defined state of 1 for the bistable multivibrator calls for Q_1 to be cut off and for Q_2 to be on. If B_0 is in its 1 state, then there is not sufficient voltage available at the collector of Q_1 to overcome the reverse bias applied to Q_3; therefore,

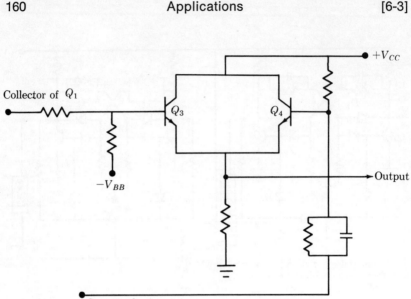

Figure 6-9. Transistorized AND gate for gating a binary counter.

Q_3 is cut off. When a negative count pulse is applied to the base of Q_4, both transistors are cut off, giving us a negative output pulse.

In general, most binary counters consist of the counters discussed earlier. Only when extremely high speed operation is required are gated counters used.

6-3   Shift Registers

In the arithmetic section of the computer, there are many circuits that either store a binary number or manipulate the number around the binary point. These circuits are simply referred to as *registers*. Because the storage is very temporary, sometimes only for a few microseconds, these registers usually consist of bistable multivibrators. A particular type of register that can shift a binary number either right or left of the binary point is called a *shift register*. Shifting a number to the left of the binary point is multiplication by 2 for each shift. Repeated division by 2 is had when a number is shifted to the right of the binary point.

Shifting can be done by causing all bistable units to transfer their contents from one to the next, simultaneously. This is called a *broadside* shift.

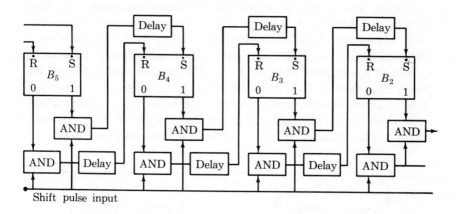

Figure 6-10.   Broadside shift register.

A block diagram of such a shift register is shown in Figure 6-10. The reader will note that we are shifting information from the highest significant bistable to the least significant one. This is a right shift, and results in division. There are delay lines shown between the output of the AND gates and the set and reset inputs of the bistable multivibrators. These delay lines are needed in order to overcome the "race" problem. By "race" we mean that the operation of the shift register will be unreliable unless we can insure that the contents of one bistable multivibrator are transferred to the next one before new information is stored in the first bistable multivibrator. The reader will note that the diagram indicates only set and reset inputs, and also indicates that there are definite 0 and 1 output points from the bistable multivibrator. Although these defined conditions for 0 and 1 are arbitrary, we must be consistent throughout the register.

The operation of the circuit is easily followed. When a shift pulse is applied, only those AND gates that have 1 inputs from the bistable circuits will operate. These gates will then supply pulse inputs to either the set or reset inputs of the next bistable circuit, thus transferring the contents of one bistable circuit to the next one. For example, assume that the number in the register is 101000. This means that the register contains the binary number equal to 40. The right-hand AND gates of B_5 and B_3 have 1 inputs from the bistables, while the left-hand AND gates of B_4 and B_2 have 1 inputs from the bistable multivibrators. When a shift pulse is applied, the AND gates supply output to the delay lines and from the delay lines to the next lower bistable. In this example the right-hand AND gate of B_5 supplies a set input pulse to B_4, the left-hand AND gate of B_4 supplies a reset input to B_3, and the right-hand AND gate of B_3 supplies a set input to B_2. The number is now 010100, the binary equivalent of 20. Now the left-hand AND gates of B_5 and B_3 have 1 inputs from the bistable circuits, and the right-hand AND gates of B_4 and B_2 have 1 inputs. When a shift pulse is applied, a reset pulse goes from B_5 to B_4, a set pulse from B_4 to B_3, and a reset pulse from B_3 to B_2. The number is now 001010, the binary equivalent of 10. The reader will note that Figure 6-10 does not show all of the bistable multivibrators of the register; the register shown in the figure illustrates only four digits of the binary number. A schematic diagram of the actual circuitry for B_5 and B_4 is shown in Figure 6-11.

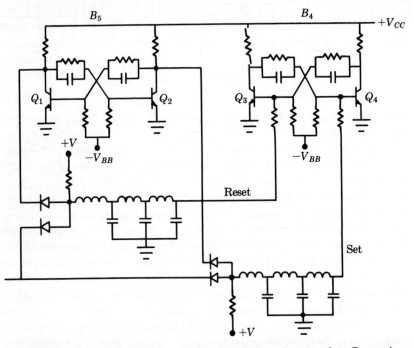

Figure 6-11. Schematic diagram of the circuits for B_5 and B_4 in a broadside shift register.

A shift register that avoids the "race" problem and, therefore, needs no delay lines makes use of a shift technique known as *ripple shift*. In this case the bistable circuits switch states one at a time, with each bistable multivibrator transferring its contents into the next one; hence, the shift "ripples" through the register. The example of *broadside* shift demonstrated *division*; let us now use an example of *ripple shift* to demonstrate

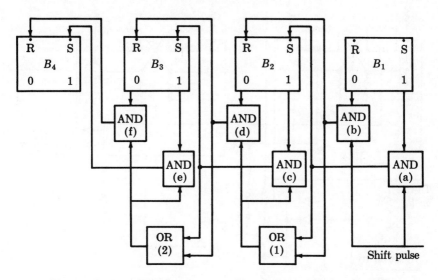

Figure 6-12. Shift register using ripple shift to the left.

multiplication. The block diagram of a ripple shift register is shown in Figure 6-12.

When a shift pulse is applied, it is applied only to AND gates (a) and (b). Only one of these gates can operate, depending upon the state of B_1. The AND gate that operates then supplies a set or reset pulse to B_2 and a pulse to OR gate (1). The pulse to OR gate (1) supplies pulses to AND gates (c) and (d). Either (c) or (d) will provide an output pulse, depending on the state of B_2. The output pulse will then either set or reset B_3 and provide a pulse to OR gate (2). OR gate (2) supplies pulses to AND gates (e) and (f), sensing the state of B_3, and causing the contents of B_3 to be transferred to B_4. The circuitry of the ripple shift register for B_1 and B_2, along with the associated logic gates, is shown in Figure 6-13. In this circuit the shift pulse is a *positive* pulse. If we agree that a bistable multivibrator is its 1 state when the right-hand side is in cutoff, then when the shift pulse is applied, AND gate (a) operates. This provides a positive set pulse to Q_4, transferring the 1 from B_1 to B_2. At the same instant, the output of AND gate (a) is applied to the diode OR gate (1). The output of the OR gate provides a positive pulse to the emitter follower, which then supplies a positive pulse to AND gates (c) and (d). One of these will then provide output to B_3. The reader will note that the shift pulse must also supply a reset input to B_1, switching it to the 0 state.

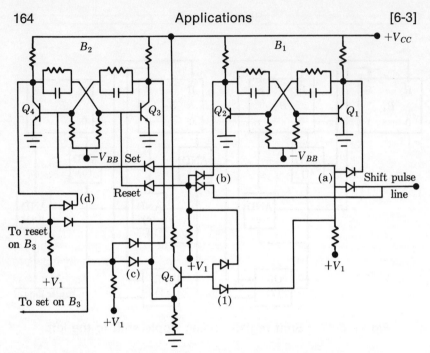

Figure 6-13.   Circuit for B_1 and B_2 of the ripple shift register
of Figure 6-12.

Binary counters can be made to operate to any scale. It is common
practice to use binary counters as a scale-of-10 counter. In order to do
this, a scale-of-16 counter is modified. In some cases feedback is supplied
so that the count is advanced by 6, causing decimal number 9 to appear
in the counter as binary number 15. Then with the tenth pulse, the counter resets to zero. Another technique is to use an AND gate to supply a
reset to the counter when the counter is at the binary equivalent of 10.
We shall merely look at block diagrams of both types. A feedback type
of scale-of-10 counter is shown in Figure 6-14. For the first seven pulses,
the count proceeds in exactly the same manner as in a scale-of-16 counter.
At the end of the seventh pulse the binary number is 0111. The only bistable circuit with a 0 is B_3. At the eighth pulse, bistables 0 through 2
switch to the 0 state, and B_3 switches to the 1 state. A set pulse is fed
through a delay line to bistables B_1 and B_2. The counter now contains
1110, which would be equivalent to decimal number 14. Although only
eight pulses have been put into the counter, the states of the bistable multivibrators are as if fourteen pulses have been counted. At the ninth pulse,
B_0 switches to the 1 state, filling the register. At the tenth pulse, the counter resets to 0 for all bistable multivibrators.

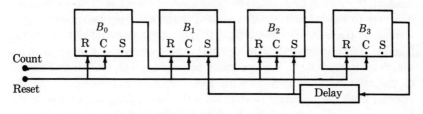

Figure 6-14. Scale-of-10 binary counter using feedback to advance the count.

Figure 6-15 illustrates the use of an AND gate to reset all bistable multivibrators to the 0 state with the tenth count pulse. Since the binary equivalent of 10 is 1010, the 1 output sides of B_1 and B_3 supply inputs to the AND gate, causing it to produce an output pulse that is used as a reset to all stages. In actual practice the gate is a NAND gate, because an off pulse is more effective in switching the bistable multivibrator.

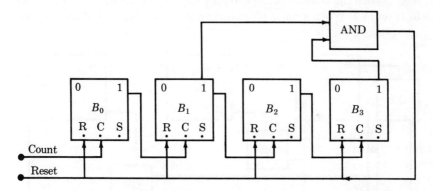

Figure 6-15. Scale-of-10 binary counter using AND gate for feedback.

6-4 Ring Counters

In the ring counter, only *one* bistable circuit is permitted to be in the 1 state at any particular instant. All other bistable units must be in the 0 state. The name of the counter is derived from the fact that the output of the last multivibrator is connected to the set input of the first bistable multivibrator. The circuit is primarily used for decimal readout from a binary counter, as there is no need for matrixing circuits in order to decode binary numbers into decimal form. When the ring counter is used for readout, there must be as many bistable multivibrators as there are decimal numbers to read. Each bistable multivibrator has only two trigger input terminals; there is no symmetrical trigger input terminal. At reset, the bistable unit corresponding to decimal 0 is set into the 1 state, with all others set to the 0 state. When a count pulse is applied, the 1 is transferred to the next bistable circuit. With each count, the 1 moves along the counter until the last state is at 1. With the next count, the output of the last stage sets the first bistable back to 1, indicating that a count through the entire scale of the register has been completed. A block diagram of a basic ring counter is shown in Figure 6-16. The scale of the counter is 5. The reader will note that the count input is applied to all of the units of the counter. A count input is a reset input. Output from one bistable multivibrator to the next is obtained when a bistable multivibrator switches from the 1 state to the 0 state. The basic circuit shows the use of OR gates at the inputs of some of the bistable circuits. This is done so as to isolate the reset line from the input sources.

Let us now follow the operation of the ring counter through several steps. When the counter is reset, B_1 through B_5 are set to the 0 state, and B_0 is set to 1. When a pulse is applied on the count line, all of the bistable

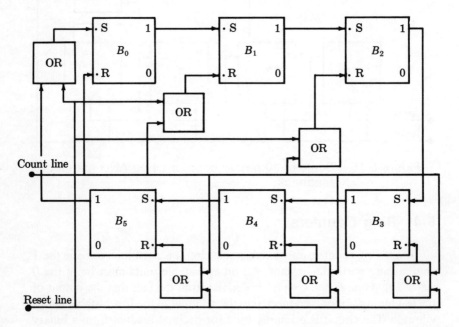

Figure 6-16.   Ring counter.

multivibrators are set to the 0 state. In order for B_0 to reset to 0, it must shift from 1 to 0. This provides a set output to B_1. Upon the next count pulse, B_1 shifts to 0, supplying a set trigger to B_2. Similarly, each count pulse causes the 1 to advance to the next highest bistable circuit. After five count pulses, B_0 through B_4 are in the 0 state, and B_5 is in the 1 state. At the sixth pulse, B_5 shifts from 1 to 0, transferring a set pulse to B_1 and returning the counter to its initial, reset state.

The stability of the ring, when used at high speeds, is increased if AND gates are added to the circuit. The AND gates are used to advance the 1 from bistable to bistable multivibrator. In this circuit, shown in Figure 6-17, the count input is applied to the AND gates. The gates then sense the state of the preceding bistable circuit, and only one gate supplies a pulse so as to transfer the 1 to the next bistable multivibrator. In addition, the AND gate that operates must reset the bistable circuit that previously held the 1. The circuit still requires OR gates at the reset inputs of the multivibrators in order to prevent pulse transfer into the reset line while the counter is operating. The block diagram of the circuit is for a scale-of-3 counter.

Let us pick up the operation of the counter of Figure 6-17 after two count pulses have been applied. B_0, B_1, and B_3 are in their 0 states, and the 1 is located in B_2. When the third count pulse is applied, the only AND

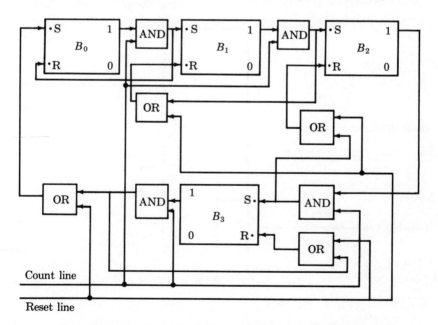

Figure 6-17.   Ring counter using OR and AND gates.

gate to operate is the one connected between B_2 and B_3, as this is the only one with inputs to both terminals of the gate. The output of the AND gate switches B_3 to the 1 state and resets B_2 to the 0 state. When the next count pulse is applied, the AND gate at the output of B_3 operates, setting B_0 to 1 and resetting B_3 to 0. The ring counter has now completed a full cycle of count, and is in the same state as if we had applied a reset pulse to the counter.

6-5 Gating Circuits

Switching circuits may be used in conjunction with oscillators and amplifiers so as to control the operation of the linear circuit over precisely determined time intervals. In such applications the output voltage level of the switching circuit determines whether or not the linear circuit has proper operating voltages in order to permit operation.

Several gating techniques may be used. In all cases, the switching circuit functions so as to cut off the operation of the amplifier until the desired input signals are presented to the switching circuit. The circuit of

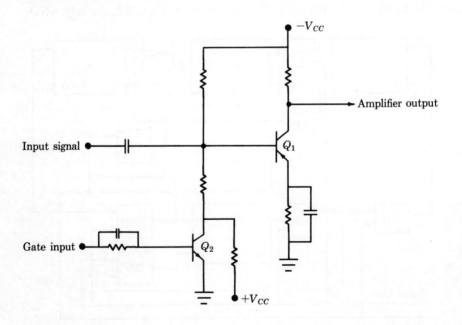

Figure 6-18. Base circuit gating of an amplifier.

Figure 6-18 is a gating method using the V_{CE} of the switching transistor as a cut-off bias on a transistor amplifier.

In the absence of a gate signal, Q_2 is in cutoff. The high positive voltage at its collector prevents the PNP transistor amplifier from operating. When a gate pulse is applied, Q_2 is driven into saturation, effectively returning the base circuit of the amplifier to ground and enabling the forward-bias circuit of the amplifier to become operative.

The circuit of Figure 6-18 requires the use of two power supplies. Another gating method makes use of the emitter circuit. In this method another transistor of the same type as the amplifier is placed in series with the emitter circuit. When the gating transistor is in cutoff, a high reverse voltage appears between the emitter terminal of Q_1 and ground. The amplifier operates only when the gating transistor is in saturation, for at this time the low saturation resistance of the gating transistor closes the emitter circuit. A circuit of this type is shown in Figure 6-19.

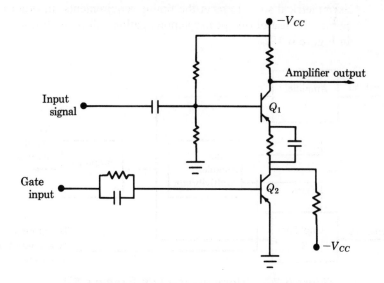

Figure 6-19.   Emitter gating of an amplifier.

It is possible to arrange circuits so that the amplifier is operative until a gating pulse is applied. However, this form of gating can result in a rectified output from the amplifier if input signals are large enough. For example a CE circuit could be arranged so that the forward bias is obtained from a gating circuit. Then when a gating pulse is applied, forward bias for the amplifier is removed. If the amplifier is handling a-c signals, the input signals will cause the amplifier to conduct during the portions of the input cycles that forward bias the transistor amplifier.

The remainder of this section will now be devoted to some interesting and challenging examples of use of gating circuits.

Example 6.3. Design a system so that two different signals may be seen on an oscilloscope, using the same base line on the scope for both signals. Let one signal be displayed for 200 μsec and the other for 300 μsec.

Solution:

(a) Sketch a block diagram of the proposed system. (Figure 6-20) Although amplifier 3 is not necessary for the solution of the problem, it has been included in order to illustrate how the separate signals are developed in sequence across a common load. The 2-kc/s astable multivibrator was selected because the total time of a "cycle" of operation is 500 μsec. The multivibrator will be asymmetrical so as to meet the timing requirements. In order to permit the use of one power supply, gating will be performed as in Figure 6-19.

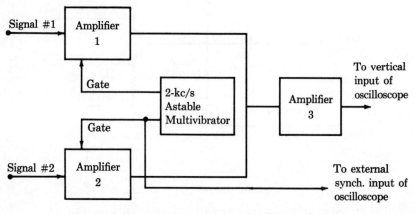

Figure 6-20.   Block diagram for Example 6.3.

(b) Design the multivibrator. Because of the low frequency of operation, any general purpose transistor will be suitable. To simplify the problem, let us use the same type of NPN transistor for the multivibrator and the amplifiers.

(1) The system shall use 2N358A transistors.

$$V_{CC} = 15 \text{ v}, \; h_{FE(\min)} = 40, \text{ and } I_{C(\text{sat})} = 6 \text{ ma}.$$

(2) Use the procedures outlined in Chapter 4.

$$R_L = \frac{V_{CC}}{I_{C(sat)}} = 2500 \ \Omega$$

$$R_B = h_{FE(min)}R_L = 100 \ K\Omega$$

$$C_1 = \frac{T_1}{0.69 \ R_B} = \frac{200 \times 10^{-6}}{0.69 \times 10^5} = 2800 \ pf$$

$$C_2 = \frac{T_2}{0.69 \ R_B} = \frac{300 \times 10^{-6}}{0.69 \times 10^5} = 4350 \ pf$$

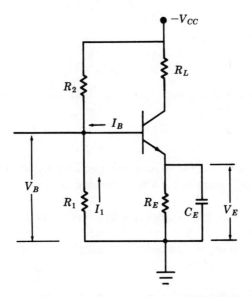

Figure 6-21.   Amplifier circuit for Example 6.3.

(c) Design the individual amplifier stages. Let all three stages be of the type shown in Figure 6-21.

(1) With V_{CC} equal to 15 volts, we shall use a total collector circuit resistance of 1800 Ω. Of this resistance, 1200 Ω will be collector load resistance, while 600 Ω will be used in the emitter circuit for stabilization of the Q point.

(2) A load line is then drawn on the average collector characteristics of the 2N358A. Let us decide to use a $V_{CE(Q)}$ of 5 volts. $I_{C(Q)}$ is then read from the characteristics. $I_{C(Q)} = 5.6$ ma and $I_{B(Q)} = 60 \ \mu a$.

(3) Assume that $V_{BE(Q)} = 300$ mv.

(4) Let $I_1 = 10 I_B$. (The larger that I_1 is with respect to I_B, the greater the stability of the operating point.)

$$I_1 = 600 \ \mu a$$

(5) Solve for R_1.

$$R_1 = \frac{V_B}{I_1} = \frac{V_{BE} + V_E}{I_1}$$
$$= \frac{0.3 + 600 \times 5.66 \times 10^{-3}}{0.6 \times 10^{-3}}$$
$$= \frac{3.7}{0.6 \times 10^{-3}} = 6180 \ \Omega$$

(6) Solve for R_2.

$$R_2 = \frac{V_{CC} - V_B}{I_B + I_1} = \frac{11.3}{0.66 \times 10^{-3}} = 17.1 \ K\Omega$$

(7) C_E is determined by the low frequency requirements of the amplifier.

$$C_E = \frac{10}{2\pi f R_E}$$

(d) The entire system can now be interconnected as in the block diagram of Figure 6-20. The completed circuit is shown in Figure 6-22. The reader will note that the collectors of the transistors in the multivibrator are being used as emitter gates for the amplifiers 1 and 2. When one of the transistors of the multivibrator is in saturation, the amplifier associated with that transistor is permitted to operate.

Example 6.4. A sequential sampling system is to be arranged so that the output of line A is sampled for 10 μsec, then line B output for 8 μsec, and then line C output for 15 μsec. After line C sampling is completed, the cycle must start up again at A. Design two possible systems.

Solution I.

One solution to the problem is shown in block form in Figure 6-23. In this system the astable multivibrator is the basic timing device. Trigger from the astable multivibrator is coupled to monostable multivibrator No. 1. Monostable multivibrator No. 1 supplies a 10-μsec gate for amplifier A. At the end of the 10-μsec interval, monostable multivibrator No. 1 supplies a trigger pulse to No. 2, which gates amplifier B for 8 μsec. At the end of the 8-μsec period, No. 2 supplies a trigger pulse to monostable multivibrator No. 3, which then gates line C amplifier for 15 μsec. At the end of the controlled interval the

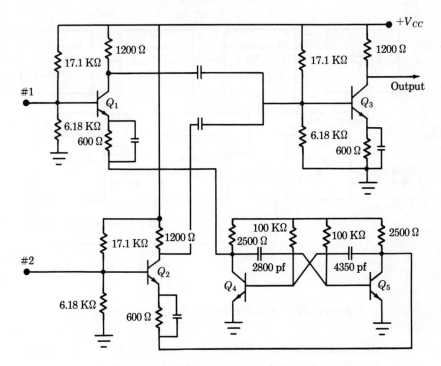

Figure 6-22. Completed circuit for Example 6.3.

astable multivibrator again triggers No. 1, which starts a new sampling cycle.

(a) Type 2N404A PNP transistors shall be used for the multivibrators. Let $V_{CC} = -20$ v, $I_{C(sat)} = 25$ ma, and $h_{FE(min)} = 24$.

(b) Design the astable multivibrator.

    (1) $R_L = \dfrac{V_{CC}}{I_{C(sat)}} = 800 \ \Omega$

    (2) $R_B = h_{FE(min)} R_L = 19.2 \ \text{K}\Omega$

    (3) Let $C_1 = C_2 = \dfrac{T}{0.69 \ R_B}$. T in this problem is one-half the time of one cycle.

$$C_1 = C_2 = \frac{16.5 \times 10^{-6}}{0.69 \times 19.2 \times 10^3} = 1245 \ \text{pf}$$

(c) Design the monostable multivibrators. With the exception of the capacitors used for the timing of the quasi-stable periods, all of

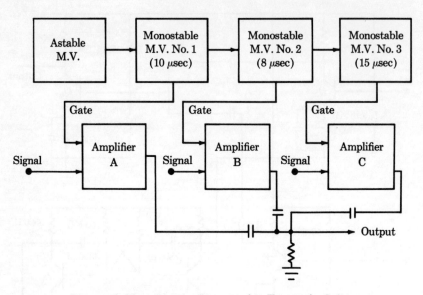

Figure 6-23. Block diagram for Example 6.4.

the monostable multivibrators are the same. Let us use an externally biased type, with V_{BB} equal to $+1$ volt.

(1) $R_L = \dfrac{V_{CC}}{I_{C(\text{sat})}} = 800\ \Omega$

(2) $R_{B2} = h_{FE(\text{min})} R_L = 19.2\ \text{K}\Omega$

(3) $I_B = \dfrac{I_{C(\text{sat})}}{h_{FE(\text{min})}} = 1.04\ \text{ma}$

(4) Let $I_2 = 0.1\ I_B = 104\ \mu\text{a}$

(5) $R_2 = \dfrac{V_{BB} + V_{BE}}{I_2}$ \qquad (Assume that $V_{BE} = 300\ \text{mv}$)

$\qquad = 12.5\ \text{K}\Omega$

(6) $R_1 = \dfrac{V_{CC} - V_{BE}}{I_B + I_2} = 18.8\ \text{K}\Omega$

(7) $C_2 = \dfrac{10^{-6}}{R_1} = 53\ \text{pf}$

(8) Solve for C_1 in the various monostable circuits.

Monostable No. 1:

$$C_1 = \frac{10^{-5}}{0.69 \times 19.2 \times 10^3} = 755\ \text{pf}$$

Monostable No. 2:

$$C_1 = \frac{8 \times 10^{-6}}{0.69 \times 19.2 \times 10^3} = 604 \text{ pf}$$

Monostable No. 3:

$$C_1 = \frac{15 \times 10^{-6}}{0.69 \times 19.2 \times 10^{-3}} = 1130 \text{ pf}$$

(d) The actual design of the amplifiers is not *germane* to the problem, since no performance specifications were stated. If we assume that the amplifiers are for the audio frequency range, any CE circuit using PNP transistors is suitable.

(e) The circuit of the entire switching system is shown in Figure 6-24.

Solution II.

In this solution we are essentially making use of the same circuit as in Solution I. However the astable multivibrator is eliminated. Only a *start* pulse is fed to monostable multivibrator No. 1. In order to make the system recycle, a trigger pulse is coupled to monostable multivibrator No. 1 from monostable multivibrator No. 3. This solution is shown in block form in Figure 6-25.

The circuit for this solution to the problem is shown in Figure 6-26. The reader will note that the amplifiers are being gated in the collector circuits. So long as the monostable multivibrator associated with the amplifier is in its stable state, the amplifier has negligible collector supply voltage because the diode is forward biased. In addition, there is a small, reverse-biased voltage at the base to insure that the transistor is in cutoff. When the monostable multivibrator is triggered into its quasi-stable state, the diode is back biased, permitting the amplifier to operate.

A brief discussion of the operation of both circuits is in order at this point. The monostable circuits are triggered by a positive pulse. Whenever one of the multivibrator transistors swings *from cutoff into saturation,* a positive pulse is developed. In the circuit of Solution I whenever the right-hand transistor of the astable multivibrator goes into saturation, a positive trigger is coupled into monostable multivibrator No. 1. This pulse causes the right-hand transistor of the monostable multivibrator to go from saturation into cutoff. This produces a negative pulse which has no effect on monostable No. 2. At the end of the 10-μsec period, the right-hand transistor of monostable No. 1 goes back into saturation, supplying a positive trigger to monostable No. 2, switching it into its quasi-stable state. During the quasi-stable period of monostable No. 1, the left-hand side was in

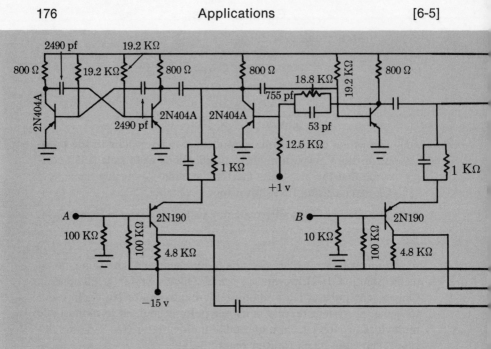

Figure 6-24.   Completed circuit for Example 6.4.

saturation, permitting amplifier A to operate. The process of triggering and gating continues through the remaining monostable multivibrators and amplifiers. At the beginning of another cycle of the astable multivibrator, the entire sampling process starts again.

In the circuit of Solution II, a positive trigger must be supplied from some external source to monostable multivibrator No. 1. After this, the gating and triggering sequence follows that of Solution I, except that the gating voltage is taken from the right-hand sides of the monostable multivibrators.

In Example 6.4 we observed the application of switching and gating to a problem requiring a timed sequence of operations. Let us now look at a problem involving gating, but with the gating as a function of logical control inputs.

Example 6.5.   Design a switching system so that if control inputs *A* and *B* are present, an output is obtained from one channel only. If control inputs *A*, *B*, and *C* are present, then output is not permitted from the first channel but must be obtained from another channel. The inputs to the channels are signals from various transducers.

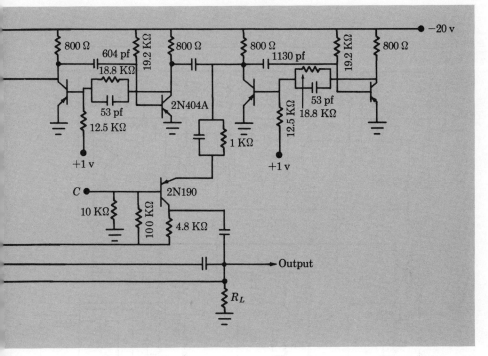

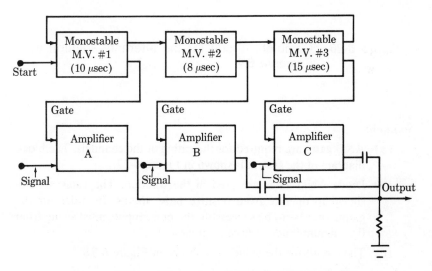

Figure 6-25. Alternate solution for Example 6.4.

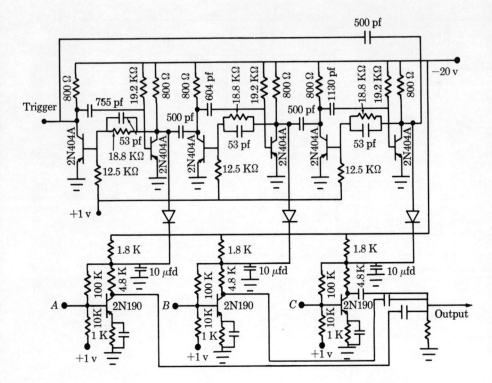

Figure 6-26. Complete circuit for the alternate solution to Example 6.4.

Solution:

(a) AND gates are required for the gating of the channels. The block diagram of the system is shown in Figure 6-27.

(b) Diode AND gates are used in the solution. The gates are designed to operate from positive pulse inputs. In order for the gating process to be successful, the pulse inputs must swing from 0 to an amplitude at least as great as V_{cc}.

(c) The circuit for the solution is shown in Figure 6-28.

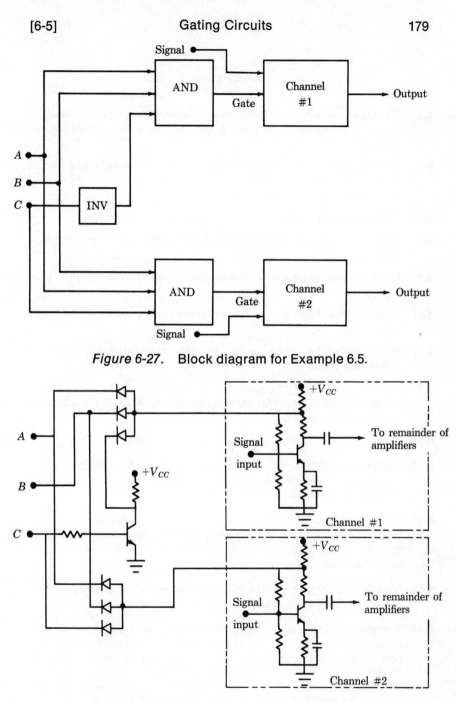

Figure 6-27.   Block diagram for Example 6.5.

Figure 6-28.   Circuit solution to Example 6.5.

PROBLEMS

6.1. Use logical circuitry to show a system that will transfer the contents of a scale-of-16 register to another register upon the application of a transfer pulse.

6.2. Design a scale-of-16 counter. Use type 2N388 transistors. Let $V_{CC} = + 15$ v, $h_{FE(min)} = 60$, and $I_{C(sat)} = 30$ ma. Let $V_{BB} = -2$ v. Use base triggering with hybrid steering.

6.3. Repeat Problem 6.2 for the circuit of Figure 6-7.

6.4. Draw a block diagram of a 6-unit broadside shift register showing how left shift would be accomplished.

6.5. Draw a schematic diagram of a three-unit register showing broadside shift to the left.

6.6. Draw a block diagram of a 5-unit ripple shift register showing a right shift.

6.7. Show how a binary counter can be made to count down (subtract) rather than count up.

6.8. Show how a scale-of-16 counter can be made into a scale-of-10 counter without the use of an AND gate to control feedback. Draw the schematic diagram of the circuit.

6.9. Draw the schematic diagram of the circuit of Figure 6-16.

6.10. An electronic switch permits two signals to be observed on an oscilloscope at the same time. Sketch a block diagram of a system that would perform this function.

6.11. The READ-WRITE operation of a computer core memory is a timed sequence operation. Let READ time and WRITE time each equal 3 μsec. Sketch a system that will gate the appropriate amplifiers when a start pulse is applied.

6.12. Show how AND gates may be used as a decoder so that a binary counter can provide decimal readout.

6.13. A system requires that an output be obtained from one channel upon the application of a control pulse. Two milliseconds after the application of the control pulse, a second channel must be gated to provide output for 50 μsec. Draw the schematic diagram of the system. Use PNP transistors. Let $V_{CC} = -25$ v, $V_{BB} = +1.5$ v, $h_{FE(min)} = 40$, and $I_{C(sat)} = 15$ ma.

6.14. Given the system shown in Figure 6-29. Design the system so that if a
pulse is applied at the X input, amplifier A provides output for 5 μsec.
If pulses are applied at both the X and Y inputs, then amplifiers A, B,
and C are sampled in sequence for 100 μsec each. If a pulse is applied
only to the Y input terminal, then no outputs from any of the amplifiers
are permitted.

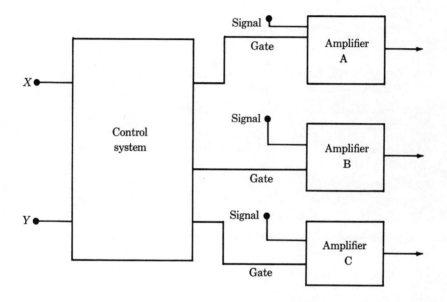

Figure 6-29.   System for Problem 6.14.

INDEX

Active region, 16
AND gates:
  and binary counters, 164-165
  and ring counters, 167
  use of to increase speed of counters
    (*see* Counters, speed of)
AND logic:
  use of tunnel diode to perform,
    122-124
Astable circuit:
  definition of, 64
Astable multivibrators (*see* Multivibrators, astable)

Bistable circuit:
  definition of, 64
  and tunnel diode, 122
Bistable multivibrators (*see* Multivibrators, bistable)
Blocking oscillators, 105-112
  astable circuit, 105, 106-110
  diagrams of, 105, 106, 107, 108,
    109, 111, 112
  monostable circuit, 105, 110-112
    diagram of, 111
Boolean algebra:
  and simplification of equations, 9-
    12
  solutions of logic circuits by means
    of, 53-62
Broadside shift (*see* Shift registers)

Collector current clamping (*see*
  Switches, non-saturated)
Collector voltage clamping (*see*

Switches, non-saturated)
Commutating capacitors, 99
Counters, 151-160
  binary counters, 152-160
    and AND gates, 164-165
    and NAND gates, 165
    coupling of bistable circuits,
      155-156
  ring counters, 165-168
    and AND gates, 167
    and OR gates, 167
    operation of, 166-168
  speed of, 157-160
  triggering of, 151
  use of in bistable multivibrators
    (*see* Multivibrators, bistable)
Cut-off region, 16

De Morgan's theorem:
  applications of, 8, 11, 56, 60
  proof of, 7
  statement of, 7-8
Diode-transfer logic, 44
Double diode clamping (*see* Switches,
  non-saturated)

Flip-flop, 86
Fulldriven operation, 17

Gating circuits, 168-178
  use of, 170
Gating techniques, 168-170

Hybrid timing circuits, 140-148

183